Teaching Mathematics to Slow Learners

Aileen Duncan

Ward Lock Educational

ISBN 0 7062 3666 1

Reprinted 1981

Printed by Hollen Street Press Ltd
for Ward Lock Educational
47 Marylebone Lane, London W1M 6AX
A Pentos Company
Made in Great Britain

CONTENTS

INTRODUCTION

This book is intended to help any student or teacher who is concerned with primary mathematics, whether they teach in a primary school or work with slow learners in the secondary school.

Part One looks at the content of the curriculum, the learner and the methods which can be adopted to allow a pupil at the level of concrete operations to master the abstract world of mathematics. Assessment and links with the secondary school are also considered.

Part Two sets out a highly structured mathematics programme, giving objectives, which are the pupils' goals, and methods by which the objectives might be attained.

Throughout the programme it is suggested that mathematical concepts are introduced to the pupil in a practical context through the use of materials. The pupil is encouraged to describe what he is doing, and the language he uses will provide him with an understanding of number manipulation long after concrete materials have been abandoned.

Games are given particular emphasis. Most of them require only a dice and a set of cards on which numerals have been written. These games provide the stimulation and practice which the slow learner especially requires to learn and remember number facts.

My sincere thanks are due to William Dunn of the Education Department of Glasgow University, members of the Scottish Education Department Inspectorate, colleagues at Hamilton College of Education, the personnel of the Mathematics Resource Centres Job Creation Project, as well as to the many teachers and pupils of primary schools in Strathclyde Region, for their help in developing and testing the material used.

Aileen Duncan
Hamilton

PART ONE
Objectives and rationale

CURRICULUM CONTENT

The main concerns of primary mathematics today are to:

1 give the pupil an insight into the structure of the number system
2 equip the pupil with computational expertise
3 stimulate the pupil's conceptual development of his physical environment
4 provide opportunities for the pupil to use numbers in a physical context.

Obviously under 1 we are trying to encapsulate the development of some ten thousand years in the space of a few years. However, given a concrete simulation, it is perhaps just possible to do this.

The development of the number system is admirably recorded in *Number, the Language of Science* by Tobias Danzig (1954). There he suggests that a place-value system followed immediately on the establishment of the cardinalities 'one' and 'two'. The present place-value system in base ten is the basis of all computation and it is this structure and its concrete representations which are used in this book. It is hoped in this way to give pupils a secure foundation in concepts as well as in number-manipulation skills.

Number is an abstract world whereas man has a physical environment. These worlds are linked through the application of number in the measurement of physical quantities. For example, in the case of area the learner requires an appreciation of surface before he can cover it with square units; in the case of volume he requires the maturity to recognize three-dimensional space inside containers, as well as that taken up by objects, before he can use such labels as 'a volume of about 4000 cubic centimetres'.

Such conceptual development is needed before any aspect of measure can be meaningfully quantified. The inclusion of practical measure and shape work in the primary curriculum gives the opportunity for the child to develop physical concepts, for example that a liquid takes the shape of its container, that one substance can displace another, that materials can vary in density, as well as demonstrating to him that the application of number to physical quantities is essentially approximate.

Mathematics lends itself to a highly-structured presentation where the learner can develop his own conceptual framework and skill in manipulation. This should release both the teacher and the slow learner from the pressure and dictatorship of the mathematics textbook. The days of

'Here is the maths textbook for your class for this session, Miss Jones', should be over. The teacher's objective of completing the book before the end of the session was achieved by having all the pupils making their way through the pages at the same time. This does not fit the demands of the pupils' ability range nor the aims of our present education system. The teacher must know *what* she wishes to teach. This does not just mean that she compiles a list of topic headings, although this is a beginning. Ideally the staff should get together and construct their own detailed programme of work. The teacher can then consult a pupil's previous teacher, as well as make her own assessment of his present knowledge, and so select an appropriate starting point in the structured programme. She can note what the pupil has to achieve and select a number of texts and home-made materials which will reinforce her teaching and then consolidate the work through practice.

The mathematics programme suggested in this book is listed in terms of pupil objectives. The staff of a school may adopt or adapt these as their programme of primary mathematics. To clothe this framework, teaching notes are given. These link the objectives to previous and future work in the pupil's development, break down the objectives into small progressive steps, and suggest a variety of materials and methods.

The content of the programme is separated into the topics of *number, fractions, money, measure, shape* and *pictorial representation*. These topics are tackled by *stages* (see pages 32 to 35). At each stage the amount and complexity of work is linked to a range of number. Concepts, vocabulary and skill in computation acquired at one stage are used over and over again and extended in successive stages.

Number
In the four stages, the pupil covers the range of whole numbers from zero to one thousand and is introduced and given practice in the four operations—addition, subtraction, multiplication and division. In Stage 4 the pupils are given a glimpse of larger numbers in the hope that they might realize that the number system is infinite.

Fractions
Fractions are considered mainly as operators, e.g. one half of a circle, one quarter of a strip.

Money
Money activities are closely linked to number work.

The number content could be covered by an above average pupil in four years of primary education, approximately one stage each school session, or might be the goal of the slow learner at the completion of six or seven years of schooling. This, of course, is maximum attainment. In-

Stage	Range	Whole Numbers (Operations)		
		+	−	×
1	Prenumber 0 to 10 first to third	two or more numbers with a sum ≤10	any two numbers and an answer ≤10	repeated addition activities
2	0 to 20 first to twentieth	two or more numbers with a sum ≤20	any two numbers and an answer ≤20	repeated addition activities
3	0 to 100 first to hundredth	any two numbers and an answer ≤100; calculation of several numbers involving both addition and subtraction		2, 3, 4, 5 and 10 times 'tables'
4	0 to 1000 first to thousandth numbers greater than 1000	any two numbers and an answer ≤1000; calculation of several numbers involving both addition and subtraction		6, 7, 8, 9 times tables; any number by 2, 3, 4, 5, 6, 7, 8, 9, 10 where product ≤1000; any number by 11 to 20 where product ≤1000

dividual limits will be set by individual ability. (The table below sets out the number, fractions and money content of each stage.)

Although most teachers would consider number work to be the

Operations ÷	Fractions	Money
equal sharing and grouping activities	unequal and equal parts, wholes, halves	1p, 2p, 5p and 10p coins; 'equivalent values', addition and subtraction
equal sharing and repeated subtraction activities;	halves and quarters	more equivalent values; addition; subtraction; 'shopkeeper's change';
equal sharing and repeated subtraction linked to multiplication tables with and without a remainder	wholes, halves, quarters, thirds, fifths, eighths; mixed fractions a 'family' of equivalent fractions $\{1, \frac{2}{2}, \frac{4}{4}, \frac{8}{8}\}$	all coins; addition and subtraction; cost of 2, 3, 4, 5 and 10 of same article; equal sharing and repeated subtraction activities;
any number ⩽1000 divided by 2 to 10	fractions of quantities	£1 note; equivalent values of coins for £1; recording with a point as a separator of £s and pence; addition, subtraction, multiplication and division.

essential core of the primary mathematics course, measure and shape work should not be regarded as 'frills' only to be tackled if there is time. These topics are an important part of the pupil's conceptual development as well as an outlet for the application of number skills.

Measure

The progress in measure work is closely linked to the child's maturity. The emphasis is on a practical knowledge of the physical dimensions and the standards used to express such dimensions quantitatively. As in the number programme, the steps of development made by man throughout the ages is simulated in the objectives to be achieved by the pupil. He has to be made aware of the existence of three dimensions, make qualitative comparisons and then view the differences in quantitative terms by the use of arbitrary standards. Finally he is introduced to the metric standards.

The progress through these developmental steps varies from one aspect of measure to another. The learner finds it easiest to secure concepts, make comparisons and quantify in length, with area, volume and weight development following at a different pace.

Time

Numbers are quickly associated with time because of the common usage of clocks and watches. In fact the digital watch is leading pupils to be faced with an accuracy of recording time well beyond their grasp of the concept of time intervals.

The overall framework for the measure work is shown in the following diagram.

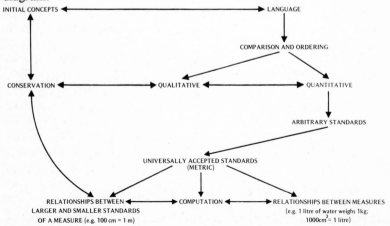

Not only does the pupil have to establish a vocabulary of measure but he also has to learn to use words associated with a dimension in the accepted context. For example, we talk about a man as 'tall', a ladder as 'long' and the top of a wall as 'high' when describing a situation involving all three.

Comparisons are initially made by placing objects side by side or one on top of the other. For example, in a set of Russian dolls, one doll can be described as taller, broader, having a greater surface area, or having a greater volume than another by being placed outside the other. Comparisons of weight cannot be made perceptually and 'feel' is deceptive and so the pupil is introduced to a balance.

Once the pupil is able to make a qualitative comparison it is suggested that the teacher carries out a conservation test in order to determine the pupil's state of conceptual development. (Such tests are dealt with on page 18 and are mentioned in the teaching notes for the programme.)

Numbers when used for measurement are essentially approximations. Each measurement is only as accurate as the scale on the tool being used will allow and it is also dependent on the care taken by the measurer. The pupil meets what might be considered as acceptable answers rather than correct ones.

Shape
A form of linear development in shape work is less easy to determine. However, initial steps are concerned with language. Too often the first shape vocabulary to which the pupil is introduced are names such as triangle, square and circle. These terms are purely labels and if presented at this time do little to help the pupil establish the basic concepts of shape. The language to be developed should describe the properties of shapes, e.g. faces, corners, flat, curved.

Three-dimensional shapes are easiest for the child to handle and so they make a good starting point. The pupil learns to discriminate between shapes by comparing one shape with another. Faces are found to be flat or curved; edges to be straight or curved and perhaps 'the same length as'; the number of faces, edges and corners are counted and compared. Just as differences are investigated, similarities can be established and then it is appropriate to introduce names of 'families' into the learning programme, e.g. cone, cube, cylinder. Two-dimensional shapes are met by the pupil as faces of three-dimensional shapes. These, in the true mathematical sense, are of course outlines on the two-dimensional plane and would not exist in a concrete form. We use 'flat shapes' i.e. plastic or cardboard representations with a minimum thickness so that the pupil can learn through touching as well as seeing. When the pupil is handling these flat shapes, it is again suggested that the language associated with properties, e.g. edge (side), corner, should be introduced before the 'family' name of triangle, square etc. Angle concepts emerge from the consideration of the shape of corners, rather than as a measure of rotation, in Stage 4.

The following diagram sets out a sequence of shape activities:

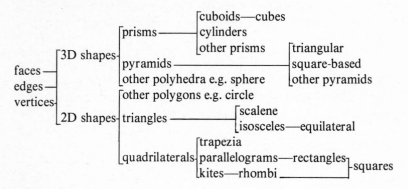

Pictorial representation

Pictorial representation is a means of recording results from number, measure and shape work. However, there is a development of understanding and skill which makes it necessary not only to include such work throughout the programme but also to develop it as a separate topic at the end of each stage.

The teacher at every stage should be aware of her own teaching aims and also of how these can be regarded as a series of pupil objectives. What we now must consider is how the learner affects such teaching.

Reference

DANZIG, T. (1954) *Number, the Language of Science* Allen and Unwin

THE LEARNER

Over the last fifty years there would seem to have been three 'fashions' in classroom learning.

First there was the *teacher-directed learning* which is usually associated with the traditional approach. The writers of the Black Papers support this view of the teacher as the source of all knowledge with the pupil as the sponge which soaks it up and then reproduces the learned facts, with techniques being perfected, though not necessarily understood, by practice.

This one-way transmission of learning was replaced in many classrooms in the 1960s by *pupil-directed learning*. This was labelled progressive education. Pupils decided what their diet of subjects would be and moved through a daily menu of integrated learning based on a theme or topic. Exhausted teachers found themselves swamped by resource material, unable to keep track of what able pupils were tackling and completely beaten in their attempts to stimulate the less able to discover for themselves. Mathematics suffered considerably in such an unstructured learning situation. However, for a less biased view of this two-way mode of learning, the reader is directed to Entwistle's (1970) book *Child-centred Education*.

In recent years a balance between these extremes has been achieved in many classrooms. This has been called *pupil-orientated learning*. Here the best of the traditional and progressive practices are welded into a partnership which gives a structured framework to learning so that both teacher and pupil know what they hope to achieve. When certain work is to be tackled and how it should be presented are decisions made by the teacher with the individual pupil in mind. These conditions are ideal for the teaching of primary mathematics. The timing of the introduction of a mathematical concept and the pace at which the pupil develops skills are vital to a slow learner's progress.

It is unlikely that the pupil just completing his first week at school will be given a reading book. The teacher is carrying out prereading activities, noting eye movements and aural and visual discrimination, as well as considering the child's oral vocabulary. Gradually over the weeks groups are formed, and those pupils whom the teacher considers ready to read embark on a structured reading programme. Mathematics must also be tackled in this way.

Prenumber activities of sorting and matching should be the pupil's first steps in preparing for mathematics. The pupil learns to recognize a property of a set of objects, e.g. redness, roundness, smallness, and is thus prepared to meet yet another property of a set—its 'how-many-ness' or cardinality. The matching of members of two sets gives the pupil a foundation for the understanding of 'as many as', 'more' and 'less'.

Most teachers know intuitively if the child is ready to read and so should also know if he is ready for number. However if there are doubts, especially with a slow learner, a Piaget-type test of conservation of number can be carried out by the teacher. Such a test highlights the child's level of maturity. The pupil is asked to:

1   match a given set of red counters with blue ones:

(If the pupil cannot carry out this task, the test is abandoned and the pupil returns to sorting and matching activities with a wider variety of materials.)

2   look at the red and blue sets of counters after the teacher has rearranged one of these sets, perhaps like this:

and consider if there are more, less or as many red counters as blue ones.

If the child thinks there are 'more' because the counters are spread out, his thinking seems to be dominated by his perception and it would be advisable to delay number work for a little while. If the child realizes that rearrangement does not alter the situation, he is more likely to be able to tackle the recognition and counting in early number work.

Conservation tests are an excellent reminder to the teacher that the child does not view the world or reason as an adult does. There is little use in rushing into a programme of mathematics when the child does not have the conceptual maturity to succeed.

All children need to learn basic number skills and to carry out practical measuring and shape activities but the slow learner should work at a pace suited to his maturity. It cannot be stated too often that pacing is the key to teaching the slow learner in comparison with his more able classmate.

The question of the pupil's 'readiness' occurs again and again. Ideally this might be solved by the teacher adapting the listed objectives into 'behavioural objectives'. These would set out for the individual pupil not only what he has to achieve but also the standard and conditions which have to be fulfilled. For example objective 36 of Stage 1 could read: '*Jim* should be able to add or subtract any two numbers where the answer is less than or equal to ten, *attaining at least three examples out of five correct on each occasion that he records calculations in his jotter*'. It is easy to recognize if such an objective has been successfully achieved and so determine if Jim should proceed to the next section or stage.

Progress based solely on success in behavioural objectives would seem to indicate that a teacher is only concerned with cognitive development. This is not so. Most teachers decide to move a pupil to new work not only because of the pupil's ability but also because of the need to stimulate interest. Sometimes a new piece of equipment or a new way of recording can arouse renewed interest in the pupil. However, in time the teacher must balance the securing of the necessary concepts and accurate computation against a satisfactory knowledge which is a basis for future improvement. This problem faces the teacher of the slow learner on many occasions and means that a careful record of the individual standard of attainment in each objective and of the difficulties left unresolved must be noted.

The time a pupil spends on a section of work is not only influenced by his ability and interest, but also by the method of teaching. The use of materials usually means slower progress, but is time well spent, especially for the slow learner.

Reference
ENTWISTLE, H. (1970) *Child-centred Education* Methuen

METHOD AND ORGANIZATION

The learning methods advocated in this book are based essentially on Piaget's theory of conceptual development in children. In the years of primary education the pupil passes from the *intuitive level* to that of *concrete operations*. A few pupils progress to the maturity of *formal operations*. The teaching of mathematics until the 1960s was directed at pupils as if they were all at the level of *formal operations*, i.e. they could reason abstractly. It is now realized that pupils in all classes of the primary school, and slow learners for all of their formal education, benefit if mathematical concepts and operations are presented initially through the use of concrete materials.

Materials

The manufacturers have met classroom needs by producing an attractive range of materials and equipment. Some of these might be regarded as gimmicks; some do not fulfil teachers' or pupils' expectations; some have become as indispensable as pencil and paper.

A set of structured number pieces come under this last category. These are physical representations of hundreds, tens and units by shapes like those in the diagram:

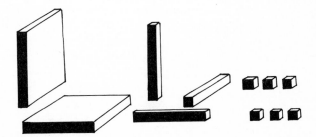

This representation is so simple and so convincing a model of the number system that it seems incredible that we have not been using it in schools over the years instead of the abacus. With the number pieces the pupil can discover the relationships between the pieces by matching. The place-value system is clarified and 'decomposition' and 'carrying' processes lose their mystery.

Numbers are represented by placing the pieces on a notation card (see page 79). Addition can be carried out by collecting together the pieces representing the numbers.

The pupil can also carry out subtraction as well as multiplication and division outside the range of the tables, e.g. 3×13 and $52 \div 4$. By renaming pieces, they can also be used to represent tens, units and tenths in decimal work. Usually the unit cube is a cubic centimetre so that the pieces are useful for measuring in length, area and volume activities.

Any equipment used must be suited to the activity and not applied merely through overenthusiasm for the material itself. And just as the material must fit the task, so must it also be related to the child's method of working. A consideration of the young learner as he tackles addition illustrates this. The pupil is presented with the problem $3 + 2$. He initially uses materials and counts like this: 'One, two, three. One, two. One, two, three, four, five. Three and two make five'. Here a unitary type of material, such as counters or cubes, is ideal. This method of calculation is slow and gradually the pupil recalls his ability to recognize the cardinality of a set. The addition can now be carried out as 'Three. Three, four, five. Three and two make five'. A material where the pieces link together has advantages here, e.g. Unifix or Pop-it beads, because the child can select a linked set of three and add two more.

To allow the child to progress towards a self-checking activity where counting can be abandoned, unmarked Cuisenaire rods or the number balance (see page 126) are excellent aids.

To really know his number bonds the pupil requires practice. Games are ideal for this because the pupil is motivated to give the correct answer quickly and there is no drudgery in this form of repetition of the number bonds.

Materials used appropriately in this way not only help the pupil to gain an understanding of the process but also lead him to the most efficient mode of calculation. It is all too common to see children counting on their fingers to find an answer. Such pupils are likely to have been rushed on to new work before having mastered each set of number facts.

At each stage of the following programme, the number bonds and concepts to be learned at any time have been carefully considered so that the slow learner has a chance of progressing from 'counting on' to knowing the number facts.

Language

Language is an essential requirement for effective learning. This must not consist of what could be called 'traditional jargon', as for example in subtraction where the technique is spoken of as 'borrowing ten' and 'paying back one'. If these expressions are related to the use of materials it is evident that they are not only meaningless but also misleading. The language which the child develops should mirror his use of materials, e.g. 'I add ten units to the top number and I add one ten to the bottom number'. Words like these aid understanding of the equal additions method of subtraction.

Division provides another example of widely-used words which convey little about the process being carried out, e.g. 'Two into five goes two and one left over'. Is the pupil finding out how many twos are contained in five? Is he sharing five equally between two? Is it even five with which the pupil is manipulating? The same language tends to be used regardless of the aspect of division being considered and whether it is five hundreds, five tens or five units. (Appropriate language for division is given on page 176.)

A model of speech should be provided for the slow learner. Ideally the pupil should be encouraged to explain what he is doing with the materials and the teacher should fashion these words into a suitable model.

Materials influence methods of calculation. This is especially true in the case of subtraction. Consider this subtraction example carried out with number pieces by two different methods:

Subtraction by the method of equal additions

$$\begin{array}{r} 4\,'2 \\ -\,1.5 \\ \hline 27 \end{array}$$

1   'Forty-two is four tens and two units. Fifteen is one ten and five units. How many more is two than five? It isn't.

2   Add ten units to the two units and one ten to the one ten. How many more is twelve than five?

3   It is seven more. How many more is four tens than two tens? It is two tens more. Two tens and seven units are twenty-seven'.

Subtraction by the method of decomposition

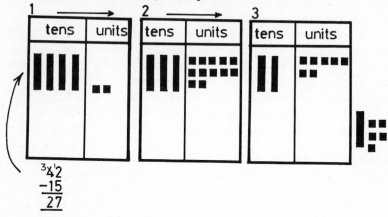

1   'Forty-two is four tens and two units.
2   I can't take five from two so I exchange one ten into ten units.
3   Five from twelve leaves seven. One ten from three tens leaves two tens. Two tens and seven units are twenty-seven'.

In the method of equal additions the pupil has to cope with the reasoning that if the same amount is added to both numbers, the difference between them remains the same. If five were added to both numbers i.e.

$$42 \xrightarrow{+5} 47$$
$$\underline{15} \xrightarrow{+5} \underline{20}$$
$$27 \qquad\quad 27$$

the subtraction calculation could easily be worked. To avoid deciding what number to add for each example the general rule is 'add ten to both numbers'. This is made more difficult for the pupil because the ten is added to the larger number (42) as ten units and to the smaller number (15) as one ten.

The language of 'take away' does not fit what the child does with the materials. He matches the units, and then the tens, bringing down the difference as the answer. The use of an expression such as 'how many more' makes us realize that the pupil is facing a difference situation which is so much more difficult than that of partitioning the number into the number to be subtracted and the answer.

In the method of decomposition the larger number only is represented by the pieces. If there are not enough units to physically take away the required number, one ten is exchanged for ten units. The pieces which are 'taken away' are left at the side of the notation card and the pieces representing the answer are left on the card.

The method of decomposition does not enable the child to be more accurate or faster in his subtraction calculations than he would be in using equal additions. Research shows that pupils taught by either method give similar results in written tests. The method of decomposition however does allow a child to understand more readily the process of subtraction and it is adopted in the teaching notes in this book.

Division work is also influenced by the use of materials. Is it possible to explain to a child why all other calculations begin by working with the units whilst in division the numeral of the highest value is the starting point? The use of materials gives the pupil a reasonable explanation.

If the units are shared equally, each share receives one and two are left. If the tens are shared, each share receives one ten and one ten is left. The

$56 \div 4$

remaining ten is exchanged for ten units and the twelve units are then shared. It is obviously much more sensible to share the larger pieces first. If any are left these can then be exchanged for smaller pieces and then the smaller pieces are all shared at the same time.

Classroom organization
If the teacher decides that learning should be optimized through practical experiences, she must realize that this decision radically influences the classroom organization. The teacher's role as a manager of resources will be challenged as she plans the daily learning programme for her pupils. The pupils will have to be grouped according to the work to be tackled and the equipment available. For example, only two or three children can work satisfactorily at a practical measuring task. The introduction of a new section of work requires the teacher to work with a maximum of six pupils so that she can have individual contact with them and focus on their problems of understanding. The other pupils will settle only if they know exactly what they have to do, have the required materials conveniently at hand and are tackling work which is suited to their ability. Mathematics is one of the easiest subjects to structure for

group learning. The integration of work on shape and measure with number allows a mixture of active work inside and outside of the classroom, and allows for a combination of discussion and recording. There is also the advantage that all pupils require practice of skills previously taught and this can be incorporated into worksheets, workcards and games. Successful group teaching is not easy to achieve. It is demanding of the teacher throughout the school day and in preparation time. However, it is effective. It allows the child to progress through an individual programme of work with the opportunity of talking and working with a few of his classmates (this is absolutely essential for the slow learner). It is rewarding for the teacher because she can note and record individual achievement.

Learning in this book is based essentially on the Nuffield Mathematics Project precept 'I do and I understand' subject always to the proviso that 'I practise and I succeed'.

ASSESSMENT AND LINKS WITH SECONDARY WORK

It is essential to keep a record of a pupil's progress. Consider this situation. David is moved to a new class at the beginning of the school session. The teacher questions him orally about his knowledge of numbers and gives him a few calculations to work. She decides that his mathematical ability is poor and he would benefit from a 'fresh start'. David can probably survive this treatment once or even twice, but repeated journeys over the same sections of work will provide little incentive to overcome previous difficulties and may make him hate the very mention of mathematics. Children, like adults, do not respond to repeated failing.

Jean's experiences in school have been very different. During the first year she found number work difficult and settled to a much slower pace than most of her classmates. By the end of the session she could recognize and record the numbers 1 to 5, nearly always added correctly in this number range and had just been introduced to subtraction as 'take away 1'. Her teacher recorded her progress on a checklist. Mostly this meant ticking boxes. Occasionally she pencilled in a note beside an item. Page 2 of this checklist is shown here:

Number 0 to 5
Reproduction of numerals 1 to 5 *occasionally still reverses 4.* ☑

Ordering of sets with cardinalities of 1 to 5 ☑

Ordering of numerals 1 to 5 (counting) ☑

'is greater than' relationships between sets of cardinalities 1 to 5 ☑
familiar with 'more than'

'is greater than' relationships between numerals 1 to 5 ☑
Jean's expression is 'bigger than'

'is less than' relationships between sets of cardinalities 1 to 5 ☑

'is less than' relationships between numerals 1 to 5 ☑

Addition

*count group know

	count	group	know
Adding 1: 1 + 1, 2 + 1, 3 + 1, 4 + 1			✓
Adding 2: 1 + 2, 2 + 2, 3 + 2		✓	
Doubles: 1 + 1, 2 + 2			✓
'Stories' of 2, 3, 4, and 5		5/	2,3 4/

Language e.g. and✓, add, plus, make✓, gives, equals ☐

Symbols e.g. ⟶✓, +, = *little formal recording yet* ☐

Subtraction

	count	group	know
Take away 1: 5 − 1, 4 − 1, 3 − 1, 2 − 1	✓		
Take away 2: 5 − 2, 4 − 2, 3 − 2			
'Stories' of 2, 3, 4, and 5			

Language e.g. take away ✓
                  leaves ✓   know ☑

Symbols e.g. − ☐

*In learning number facts the children go through stages of counting, grouping and knowing.

The checklist details objectives in fractions, money, measure, shape and pictorial representation as well as number. Jean's teacher was able to include her progress in these topics.

At the beginning of the next session Jean's new teacher consulted the checklist and decided to develop the work on subtraction. As well as teaching this new work, she prepared activities and simple games to recall numbers 1 to 5 and the addition bonds. A Bingo game was used to help Jean master the 'story of 5'.

As new progress is made it is recorded on the same checklist. A pen of a different colour is used so that the record of consecutive years can be identified.

Through such a system Jean has every opportunity of making continued progress in mathematics at a suitable pace and of gaining a sense of achievement.

When a mathematics course has been adopted by a school staff, it should be a natural consequence to compile some way of recording progress. If the course has been detailed as objectives this is relatively easy. Here are some of the objectives for measure in stage 2 showing the record of a pupil's competence.

In *length,* the pupil should be able to:

	fairly competent	competent	very competent
39 order three lengths from shortest to longest; tallest to smallest etc	☐	☐	✓
40 find how much longer, shorter, deeper, etc one object is in comparison with another, by using arbitrary standards.	☐	✓	☐

In *volume,* the pupil should be able to:

41 compare two containers to find which holds more or holds less	☐	☐	✓

These examples of checklists show that individual progress can be recorded giving detailed information about the pupil without demanding too much time and effort by teachers. Such records should be initiated in the first year of schooling and passed with the pupil from one teacher to another, and from one school to another.

Primary education is the time for developing basic concepts and skills. Secondary education may be the time for securing more concepts and skills, but it is also the time for applying previously gained knowledge. The teachers responsible for mathematics in secondary classes must provide outlets for the slow learner, allowing him to use his range of number, measure and shape experiences in a meaningful way. Here are some suggestions.

Calculators can stimulate the pupil to use and extend his number skills. A first introduction to machines can be via the hand-operated model. Here the pupil considers place value as he records each number, relates addition to subtraction by the opposing moves of the handle, finds multiplication to be repeated addition and division to be repeated subtraction. Skills of approximation are developed in order to check the machine's accuracy.

Competence with these machines can lead to the use of electronic calculators. If division is to be tackled the teacher must provide a background of decimal notation so that the form of answer recorded by the machine is understood. When the pupil is older, has had more experience with number and with the motivation of using the calculator, he may be ready to attain a further sequence of basic objectives.

Experiences with calculating machines can be stepping stones to work experiences where machines are used to record and calculate. Such work situations can be simulated in the classroom, e.g. the office with book-keeping tasks; a tailoring department with measuring and costing assignments; gardening with cost of production examples; the supermarket with stocktaking, purchasing and selling activities; and the factory where procedures are sequenced and integrated. These experiences are not only mathematics in action but also allow for discussion and follow-up visits.

As well as a preparation for work, the pupil benefits from a preparation for other aspects of adult life. The ability to budget, carry out cash transactions, take measurements for do-it-yourself plans, read timetables etc, can and should be established through practical work. A knowledge of games such as darts, draughts and dominoes should also be part of the curriculum.

This look towards the slow learner's secondary mathematics curriculum should explain the emphasis on basic concepts and manipulative skills in primary work. The pupil requires such a foundation to fulfil his potential in secondary school, otherwise he faces the prospect of that dreadful 'fresh start' and 'nose to the grindstone' with a diet of number bonds.

It is hoped that each teacher reader is now better equipped as an individual and as a member of a school staff to achieve the objective of 'guiding each pupil, through thoughtful and well-planned teaching, to attain successfully the maximum level of conceptual development and skill in computation possible for his ability'.

Teacher-expectation is a significant factor in pupil achievement. Just as the best is expected from the teacher so she in turn should insist on no less than this from the pupil.

PART TWO
The developmental mathematics programme

This part of the book sets out the objectives for the structured developmental mathematics programme.

The programme is divided into four stages, each of which sets out objectives for work in number, fractions, money, measure (volume, area, weight, time), shape and pictorial representation. (The table which follows sets out the development of these topics at the various stages.) Although the notes on number come first in each stage, work in the other topics should take place in conjunction with it.

The objectives for each topic are printed in bold, and followed by suggestions for teaching, possible materials and methods of recording.

Development of topics

NUMBER

Stage	Objectives	
1	1 to 3	*Prenumber* sorting, matching, conservation
1	4 to 17	*Numbers 0 to 5* cardinality, ordinality, numerals, addition, subtraction
1	18 to 25	*Numbers 6 to 10* cardinality, ordinality, numerals, addition, subtraction
1	26 to 41	*Numbers 0 to 10* sequences, addition, subtraction, multiplication and division activities
2	1 to 12	*Numbers 10 to 19* cardinality, ordinality, numerals, place value, addition, subtraction
2	13 to 20	*Numbers 0 to 20* sequences, addition, subtraction, multiplication and division activities
3	1 to 4	*Numbers 21 to 30* cardinality, ordinality, numerals, place value, addition, subtraction
3	5 to 15	*Numbers 31 to 99* numerals, place value, ordinal names, odd and even numbers, addition, subtraction, 2 and 3 times tables, division activities, complementary addition, differences
3	16 to 25	*Numbers 0 to 100* one hundred, sequences, number patterns, addition, subtraction, 4, 5 and 10 times tables, division linked to tables, simple word problems
4	1 to 11	*Numbers 0 to 1000* numerals, place value, addition, subtraction, multiplication by numbers 2 to 20, division by numbers 2 to 10, numbers greater than one thousand

Stage	*Objectives*	

FRACTIONS

1	42 to 44	equal and unequal parts, wholes, halves
2	31 to 33	halves, quarters, fraction notation
3	26 to 30	other fractions, mixed fractions, equivalent fractions
4	12	fractions of quantities

MONEY

1	45 to 50	recognition of 1p, 2p, 5p and 10p coins, addition and subtraction in pence, equivalent values
2	34 to 38	equivalent values, addition and subtraction (1p to 20p), shopkeeper's change with 1p coins
3	31 to 36	recognition of 50p coin, addition, subtraction and multiplication (1p to 99p), division activities with coins, shopkeeper's change with a variety of coins
4	13 to 16	introduction of £1, decimal point as separator of pounds and pence, addition, subtraction, multiplication and division (1p to £10), shopkeeper's change with pounds and pence

LENGTH

1	51 to 53	basic concepts and vocabulary, qualitative comparisons, conservation
2	39 to 40	ordering three lengths, quantitative comparisons using arbitrary standards
3	37 to 38	introduction and use of the universal standards, the metre and centimetre
4	17 to 18	personal measurements, computation

VOLUME

1	54	basic concepts and vocabulary
2	41	qualitative comparisons
3	39 to 40	conservation, quantitative comparisons using arbitrary standards
4	19	introduction and use of the universal standard, the litre

Stage	Objectives	

AREA

1	55 to 56	basic concept of surface, qualitative comparisons
2	42 to 43	conservation, ordering of three areas
3	41	quantitative comparisons using arbitrary standards
4	20	introduction and use of the universal standard, the square centimetre

WEIGHT

1	57 to 58	basic concepts of heavy and light, use of a balance
2	44	qualitative comparisons
3	42 to 43	conservation, qualitative comparisons using arbitrary standards
4	21	introduction and use of the universal standards, the kilogram and gram

TIME

1	59	sequence of events
2	45 to 46	days of the week, telling the time—hours
3	44 to 46	months of the year, telling the time—half past, quarter past and quarter to, relationships—hours, days, weeks, months and a year
4	22 to 24	telling the time to the nearest five minutes, am and pm, twenty-four hour notation

SHAPE

1	60 to 62	spatial awareness, positional vocabulary, faces of 3D shapes
2	47 to 51	edges and corners of 3D shapes, 'families' of 3D shapes
3	47 to 53	properties of 3D shapes, 2D shapes introduced as the faces of 3D shapes, properties of 2D shapes, 'families' of 2D shapes, symmetric and tiling activities
4	25 to 26	sorting 3D shapes, edges and corners of polygons (including the right angle)

Stage	*Objectives*	
PICTORIAL REPRESENTATION		
1	63	three-dimensional representations of data
2	52	pictographs
3	54	block graphs, arrow diagrams and tables
4	27	bar charts with a vertical scale

STAGE 1

Number
Stage 1 begins with prenumber activities of sorting and matching. Number work is separated into three parts: 0 to 5, 6 to 10 and 0 to 10. This allows the slow learner to recognize and reproduce numbers one to five and then use these in addition work. Subtractions such as 'two take away two' allows zero to be introduced. Having gained some confidence, the pupil is introduced to numbers six to ten and a new range of addition and subtraction facts. A third set of new facts is met when the pupil is using the full range of numbers zero to ten. Here he is also introduced to activities which begin to lay a foundation for multiplication and division.

Fractions
Fractions are introduced as a whole divided into a number of equal parts.

Money
The pupil meets and uses 1p, 2p, 5p and 10p coins in the money activities.

Measure
Basic concepts of measure are explored and given expression through language such as long, tall, full, holds more, surface, heavy and light.

Shape
Spatial awareness is linked to 'positional' vocabulary and the pupil is introduced to the faces of three-dimensional shapes.

Pictorial representation
This topic concentrates on activities involving the display of objects themselves rather than a representation of them. The importance of labelling and of discussing the representation is highlighted.

PRENUMBER
The pupil should be able to:
1 sort a universal set where
   the members are different in one way only
   the members are varied but share a common property
   the members can be partitioned into a variety of subsets

2   **match**
   familiar 'pairs' e.g. cup and saucer; bat and ball
   members of sets to find 'as many as' (equivalent sets)
   members of sets to find 'more than'
   members of sets to find 'less than'
3   **conserve number i.e. to realize that rearrangement does not change
   the cardinality (how-many-ness) of equivalent sets.**

1   Sorting a universal set

Through the activities of sorting and matching, the child can investigate
likenesses and differences between objects. He learns that a set of objects
can have a property such as redness or smallness.

Sorting can be introduced through objects which are different in one
way only. A set of cubes which are all the same colour but of two (or
three) different sizes, a set of counters which are all the same size but of
different colours, and a set of beads which are of the same colour but
different in shape, are excellent materials for the pupil to sort into a sec-
tioned tray or into boundaries made from stapled strips of card.

Many teachers like to have a 'red corner' or a 'yellow table'. This
display highlights a variety of objects which share the common property
of colour and allows the pupil to focus on likenesses in a set rather than
on differences between the members.

Having concentrated on one attribute of an object, it is now possible
to lead the children into seeing that the object has many properties. The
pupil can find a variety of properties of one member through several
sortings of the same universal set. When sorting to find red things, then
things that can roll and finally things with holes, the pupil realizes that
this bead is red, can roll, and has a hole while this cube has a hole, but is
not red and cannot roll.

In these activities the teacher has the opportunity to listen to the
child's language as he explains why members belong or do not belong to
a set. This knowledge gives scope for the introduction of new words into
the child's vocabulary e.g. more unusual colours such as brown, purple
and pink and more discriminating terms such as long, tall and large,
rather than big.

Labels for the sets can use words, but some form of picture is better.
This might be a splash of the required colour or a drawing of the shape.
If the sorting is of the child's own invention (and where possible this
should occur) encourage him to produce his own pictorial labels.

2   Matching

In sorting the child is establishing relationships. This pencil 'is the same colour as' this ball. This finding comes to light as these objects are placed in the same set of orange things. Building such relationships is the essence of the activity of matching. Probably the easiest form of matching is that of pairing familiar objects. Bread is linked to jam, the football to the football player and the child's coat to his peg.

Members of sets can be matched and the child can realize that there are relationships not only between objects but between sets of objects. If the child can build up a one-to-one correspondence between two sets he shows that they have 'as many as'. When two sets do not have the same cardinality the child has to be told that the set with unmatched members has 'more' and the other set has 'fewer' or 'less'.

These concepts are difficult for the pupil and many practical activities and recording exercises should be carried out to help lay a foundation for future understanding. Cards showing a set of people, or a set of houses or a set of trees can be used. Given sets of hats, tickets, doors, letters, apples, leaves etc, the child can match these and find that there are 'as many hats as people', 'more doors than houses' and 'fewer apples than trees'.

In recording exercises the child could be asked to match the members of two sets and then colour the set which shows more, or tick the set which shows less.

3   Conservation

Conservation as a test of readiness for number has been discussed in 'The learner'. Many teachers know intuitively if the child can proceed to number work. However, with the slower learners it is advisable to carry out a simple test of conservation of number to check that the pupil can match, can understand the phrases 'as many as', 'more' and 'less', and that he can reason that if nothing has been added or taken away, rearrangement does not change cardinality.

NUMBERS 0 to 5

The pupil should be able to:
4   recognize, name and create sets with a cardinality of two, four, three, one and five
5   recognize, name and match to the appropriate set, the numerals 2, 4, 3, 1 and 5
6   reproduce the numerals 1, 2, 3, 4 and 5

7   order sets with cardinalities of one to five
8   order number names and numerals 1 to 5 (counting)
9   recognize and create the relationships of 'is greater than' and 'is less than' between sets, number names and numerals
10   add 1, add 2, add 'doubles' i.e. $1 + 1, 2 + 2$
11   partition sets of five, four, three and two to show addition 'bonds'
12   take away 1, take away 2
13   partition sets of five, four, three and two to show subtraction 'bonds'
14   recognize, name and create an empty set; recognize and reproduce 0
15   subtract 'doubles' i.e. $5 - 5, 4 - 4$ etc
16   take away 0, and add 0
17   add and subtract any two numbers within the range 0 to 5.

4   Recognition of cardinality of sets

The pattern adopted by Fletcher (1970) in *Mathematics for Schools* of introducing early number through recognition of sets is recommended. In sorting, the child sees a set as having a property of size, colour etc and so it is a sensible step to see the set as having a property of twoness. The number sets are introduced in random order within the range of one to five at this stage to stress cardinality rather than ordinality. Members in the set have no fixed arrangement in most modern representations as opposed to the traditional introduction to arrays of dots in pairs or domino patterns. However, many teachers of slow learners retain these patterns for much of this number discrimination work, realizing that although the pupil may be able to conserve number, the concept may not be firmly grasped.

5/6   Numerals 1 to 5

Once the learner can name and form sets with a cardinality of two, four, three, one and five, attention should be turned to the corresponding numerals. The initial reproduction of any numeral should be large and on plain paper. This allows the child to use a thick writing instrument and does not demand too precise a control of hand movement. Before more formal recording in workbooks is tackled, the pupil should practise writing the numerals in large and then gradually smaller squares e.g. using 5 cm grid paper down to 2 cm squares. Very small numerals cannot reasonably be expected in this early stage. It may in fact defeat the hope of producing well-formed numerals in later years.

7   Ordering sets

Sets of concrete materials can be ordered by a matching process like this:

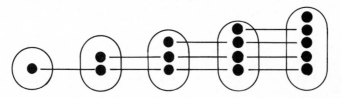

8   Counting

Numerals are then linked to the appropriate set and the 'counting order' established. It is important to try to give the child an understanding of what he means as he counts. When he says 'three', he tends to be looking at or even pointing to one object, but the name indicates all the objects counted up to that time i.e. the cardinality of the counted set. Diagrams like this should be avoided

and this format encouraged.

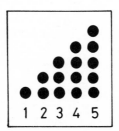

9   Relationships

Sets should be compared for 'more than' and 'less than' and then these relationships can be considered for the corresponding number names and numerals.

Rather than proceed to the numbers six to ten, it is worthwhile allowing the child to consolidate the numbers one to five by using them in the operations of addition and subtraction.

10   Adding

Let the child build up separately the two sets he is going to add. He then collects the objects together and finds the result from the newly-formed set. Unifix blocks or Pop-it beads are good materials for this.

As adding 1 is strongly linked to counting, the child should find the bonds 1 + 1, 2 + 1, 3 + 1, 4 + 1 relatively easy and gain confidence in this new aspect of the work. However, the child should not be rushed and he should be given plenty of examples using concrete materials, encouraging him to build up an associated vocabulary e.g. 'two and one make three' with the introduction of recording coming later.

Many textbooks do not use the addition symbol and the 'equals sign' at this stage. This is reasonable but two conditions must be met: the format used must be easier to understand than the traditional symbols and must not involve the child in difficulties of reproduction. This means expressions such as $(3,1) \xrightarrow{\text{add 4}}$ should be avoided and words, e.g. 4 and 1 make $\boxed{5}$, and arrows, e.g. $2 \xrightarrow{\text{add 1 makes}} 3$, should be used on worksheets where the child has only to fill in the answer.

When adding two, the pattern established for the addition of one can be followed. After the use of blocks or beads, the more abstract approach of the number line can prove useful. A line created on the classroom floor so that the children can step out the example is excellent.

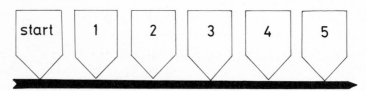

This design allows the child to take the steps on the line and still be able to read the number. '3 and 2', can become a three-step and a two-step helping the child away from counting individual steps. The intervals on the number line should not be too far apart to ensure that the child is physically capable of taking such group steps.

Until zero is introduced, the beginning is labelled 'Start'. The line should be placed so that it can be extended later for the numbers 6 to 10.

Within this range of numbers the child has only three bonds to master, 1 + 2, 2 + 2, 3 + 2, and when he moves to consider 'doubles' he has already met these facts 1 + 1, 2 + 2 and is involved in revision work. This rate of progress should make repeated success possible for even the slowest pupil.

11   Number 'stories'

The use of Cuisenaire rods brought into prominence the composition of a number. Encouraging the child to find 'stories' of a number using a variety of materials is now popular. Stories of five are much more interesting than stories of two so the numbers to be tackled are listed in the reverse order. The pupil should be given a set of blocks and asked to show two sets. A card divided into two regions or a cardboard ring with two sections is a good background for the blocks. Again, initially the work will be confined to the child using the materials and finding words to describe his findings, e.g. 'two and three make five, four and one make five' etc. Drawing results on a prepared worksheet might be a next step. The child draws a picture of his sets of counters and labels these with the appropriate numerals.

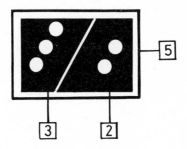

During these partitioning activities the child will find results like 'four and one make five' and 'one and four make five'. Children are unlikely to see such results as meaning that the order of numbers does not matter when adding. This fact should be pointed out when the opportunity arises so that a foundation is laid for later work on commutativity.

In the stories it should be emphasized that the new number facts the child is meeting are 2 + 3, 1 + 4, 1 + 3.

12/13   Subtracting

As long as subtraction is linked to the 'take away' aspect and concrete materials are used, most pupils find this operation just as easy as addition and some even find it easier. The child should show the larger set, partition the set to find the smaller number and then place this aside to leave the answer set. The facts dealt with at this time will be 5 − 1, 4 − 1, 3 − 1, 2 − 1, then 5 − 2, 4 − 2, 3 − 2. 'Stories' of subtraction will involve 5 − 3, 5 − 4, 4 − 3.

14/15/16   Zero

As the pupil carries out these activities he may himself wish to find the answer to a 'doubles' fact, i.e. $5 - 5$, $4 - 4$, $3 - 3$, $2 - 2$, $1 - 1$. This requires an introduction to zero. In this context, to meet the need of expressing no blocks or none left, the child finds the symbol 0 and its name zero meaningful.

The concept of zero is difficult and 'taking away 0' and particularly 'adding 0' should not be laboured at this time.

17   Computation

Before leaving this range of numbers the pupil should meet mixed addition examples, e.g. $3 + 1$, $2 + 2$, $1 + 2$, mixed subtraction examples, e.g. $4 - 0$, $3 - 2$, $1 - 1$ and then mixed addition and subtraction examples, e.g. $2 - 1$, $1 + 1$, $3 + 2$, $4 - 2$, $1 - 0$, $2 + 1$. Because of the child's level of understanding, or to make recording shorter and simpler, this might be the right time to introduce first the addition and subtraction symbols and then the equals sign. Stages of recording might be:

$$3 \text{ add } 2 \text{ makes } 5$$
$$3 \xrightarrow{\text{ add } 2 \text{ makes }} 5$$
$$3 \xrightarrow{\text{ + } 2 \text{ makes }} 5$$
$$3 + 2 \xrightarrow{\text{ makes }} 5$$
$$3 + 2 = 5$$

$$3 \text{ take away } 1 \text{ leaves } 2$$
$$3 \xrightarrow{\text{ take away } 1 \text{ leaves }} 2$$
$$3 \xrightarrow{\text{ } - 1 \text{ leaves }} 2$$
$$3 - 1 \xrightarrow{\text{ leaves }} 2$$
$$3 - 1 = 2$$

The use of the arrow allows the child to tell a story (indicated by words in the first example only) and so becomes a means of easy recording.

Some children may abandon the use of concrete materials for this number work as they gain success in examples and can find the answers more quickly. Others may require encouragement to try an example without materials. However, many children may still require the aid of one type of material, e.g. counters at the counting stage; Unifix blocks fitted together and later Cuisenaire rods or the number balance at the grouping stage. Progress from materials to the abstract should not be hurried or the pupils will resort to using their fingers and develop a habit which keeps them at the counting stage throughout their primary education.

Games

All the children should be able to cope with simple track games, e.g. using a dice with faces showing the numerals 0 to 5 to indicate to the player how many boxes to move along. The slow learners will take time to recognize their 'counter' so it is a good idea for these children to play on a longer track and move the same counter, the winner being the player who takes the counter over the finishing line. The square in which to begin counting the move is another problem for some pupils and help is required with this. This early training in playing games is most worthwhile because the children gain confidence through knowing they are making the correct responses and play more sociably in a group.

NUMBERS 6 to 10
The pupil should be able to:
18 recognize, name and create sets with a cardinality of six, seven, eight, nine and ten
19 recognize, name and match to the appropriate set, the numerals 6, 7, 8, 9 and 10
20 reproduce the numerals 6, 7, 8, 9, 10
21 order sets with cardinalities of six to ten
22 order number names and numerals 6 to 10
23 recognize and create the relationships of 'is greater than' and 'is less than' between sets, number names and numerals
24 add 1, add 2, add 0
25 take away 1, take away 2, take away 0, 'doubles' e.g. 6 − 6.

18 Sets of six to ten
Recognition of sets of cardinality six to ten is not easy perceptually and so these sets are best introduced in order so that previous counting skills can be used and extended. Time must be taken over the introduction of these sets and numerals. The child should be given the opportunity of forming sets in a large variety of materials. Beads can be threaded or 'popped' together; blocks can be built into towers; animal shapes can be enclosed in a 'field'; houses formed into a street; toy cars parked in a car park etc. By drawing and gumming pictures, pictorial representations can be made in an individual, group or class number-book. Worksheet exercises can involve the child in colouring, ticking and drawing as he recognizes required sets.

19/20 Numerals 6 to 10
Practice in reproducing the numerals should follow the suggestions for the earlier ones, i.e. the material used should be unstructured until the child's manipulation is good enough to allow him to write a numeral of a specific size.

21/22   Ordering
As for earlier numbers, the sets should be ordered by matching members and then the appropriate numerals linked to the ordered sets. Although the child has been meeting the numbers in order, this activity should emphasize counting as a series of 'adding one' steps.

23   Relationships
Children seem to find it difficult to realize that not only is seven more than six, but eight, nine and ten are also. The relationship 'less than' produces the same difficulty and so examples should be included at this stage which require more than one answer. Understanding, however, is likely to be only superficial. Work with a number line helps answer questions about 'what is the number before' and 'which number comes after' as well as producing sequences in ascending or descending order, e.g. 7, 8, 9 and 8, 7, 6.

24   Adding
Activities which give scope for a group of children of mixed ability to work together are valuable. One such activity is to create a 'computer' with an 'operator', an 'inputer' and an 'outputer'. For input, a child selects a set of objects, e.g. seven sticks, and gives them to the operator. This child today may be an 'add 1' operator so he adds one more of the same type of object. At output, another child receives the new set and finds the result of the addition. Each child may also record his part of the calculation on the blackboard or a sheet of paper. The operator's job can be given to a child who can easily manage the repetitive task, but is still having difficulty with the addition. This activity allows the children to learn from each other.

The addition bonds to be taught at this stage are: $6 + 1, 7 + 1, 8 + 1, 9 + 1, 6 + 2, 7 + 2, 8 + 2, 6 + 0, 7 + 0, 8 + 0, 9 + 0, 10 + 0$.

The child will find it difficult to select a set of six, seven, eight, nine and ten by sight. This means continual laborious counting, e.g. to calculate $7 + 2$ the child counts 1, 2, 3, 4, 5, 6, 7 then 1, 2 and to find the answer again counts 1, 2, 3, 4, 5, 6, 7, 8, 9. Boxes of beads or cubes joined together into sevens, sixes etc are ideal, because they encourage the child to select a set of 7, add 2 and then be involved only in counting to find the answer.

25   Subtracting
The sets of joined blocks and beads could also be used for subtraction examples. The subtraction bonds to be taught are: $10 - 1, 9 - 1, 8 - 1,$

$7 - 1, 10 - 2, 9 - 2, 8 - 2, 10 - 0, 9 - 0, 8 - 0, 7 - 0, 6 - 0, 10 - 10,$
$9 - 9, 8 - 8, 7 - 7, 6 - 6.$

The 'take away' aspect of subtraction is easy to carry out with concrete materials but difficult to show in a worksheet example. The 'taking away' can be achieved by hiding the drawn objects with a hand or crossing out.

This section of work has introduced the child to twelve new addition facts and seventeen new subtraction facts. A variety of fill-in recording formats should be used to give plenty of practice examples, e.g.

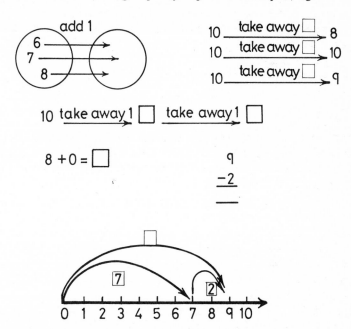

NUMBERS 0 to 10
The pupil should be able to:
26 order sets with cardinalities of zero to ten
27 order number names and numerals 0 to 10
28 recognize and create the relationships of 'is greater than' and 'is less than'
29 recognize and state sequences e.g. five, six, seven and 7, 6, 5
30 recognize and use the ordinal number names first, second and third
31 add 1, add 2, add 'doubles' e.g. 4 + 4

32   **take away 1, take away 2**
33   **partition sets of six to ten to show addition bonds**
34   **partition sets of six to ten to show subtraction bonds**
35   **carry out complementary addition involving the addition of 1, e.g.**

$$7 + \square = 8, \ 1 + \square = 6$$

36   **add or subtract any two numbers where the answer is less than or equal to ten**
37   **add three or four numbers where the sum is less than or equal to ten**
38   **build a pattern of repeated addition e.g. a 'table' of twos**
39   **build a pattern of 'doubles' (3 + 3), 'triples' (2 + 2 + 2) e.g. 'times tables'**
40   **share equally between two and among three, four and five where no remainders are involved**
41   **find how many twos (threes, fours and fives) there are.**

26   Ordering sets

Towers of blocks can be built to represent sets with a cardinality of one to ten. After they have been constructed, the child can order the towers by height. He will find he is making a stairway of steps. Matching the blocks in each set can be carried out by a colour arrangement, e.g. the first block in every tower is red, the second blue etc.

27   Ordering numerals

Numerals should be linked to the appropriate sets, perhaps as 'caps', or some other form of label, on the towers. It can be brought to the child's notice that he begins with no blocks (table level for the tower staircase) and this can be labelled 0.

The number line on the classroom floor can be extended and then stepped out by the children as they count to ten. The position of 0 can be discussed and then the symbol put in the correct place. Joining numerals in order to form a picture is another activity enjoyed by most children.

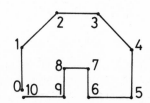

House cards can also be used.

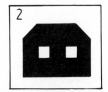 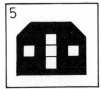 

The windows, the door and the chimneys are outlined as squares or collections of squares which can be filled with cubes. When the cubes are in position they are counted and the correct numeral card is attached to the diagram. These completed cards are then ordered from 0 to 10.

28   Order relationships

The number 'towers' can be used to consider a variety of answers to questions like 'What number is greater than 4?' or 'Which number is fewer (or less) than 8?' Visual comparison of the height of the towers will help many of the pupils.

Games

A simple game can be played using the number line. One pupil is asked to stand on number 6. Each other pupil in turn takes a card which will be MORE THAN or LESS THAN and carries out the instruction by standing on an appropriate number. Of course, other numbers can be used for the start of the game.

Another game involves a pack of cards (with jacks, queens, kings and aces removed). To play 'more than', remove three of the twos and share the other cards equally between two players. Each child plays a card from his unseen pile and the player of the higher card claims both cards and places them at the bottom of his pile. If both cards are the same, they are left to be claimed by the player of the higher of the next two cards. One player in time will use all his cards and the other player is declared the winner. If more than two children play, the game becomes 'who has the greatest (or highest) number?' If a 'less than' or the 'smallest number' version of the game is played, remove three tens instead of three twos.

29   Sequences

Some children can count efficiently if they begin at one, but find it diffi-cult to remember the order of the numbers in sequences which begin at a number other than one. Using cut-outs from a magazine or comic or by drawing, some picture series should be prepared. Allow the child to order these. To check if his order is correct he should turn the cards over and look at the numerals written on the back. If these are in ascending sequence the pictures are ordered correctly.

Game

A card game based on sequences, like Rummy, is ideal at this stage. A pack of playing cards, from which all the picture cards have been removed, is used. Each player is dealt three cards. Either by taking the top card from the pile of remaining unseen cards or by picking up the last card discarded, a player tries to build up a sequence. The first player to do so is the winner.

30   Ordinal number names

Number used in a cardinal sense states how many members there are in a set. Number used in an ordinal sense indicates the position of one member in a set. Number names one, two, three etc can be used for both aspects e.g. 'there are *three* children in the class' is an example of three used as a cardinal number; 'turn to page *three*' shows three used as an ordinal number. However at this stage of the programme we are dealing with special ordinal names. Unfortunately 'first', 'second' and 'third' are not words easily related to one, two and three. Opportunities have to be created to make this relationship clearer. Daily classroom happenings allow scope for the use of these terms, e.g. the *first* child to arrive at school, the *second* helping at school lunch, the *third* door is Mrs Grant's room. 'First' should also be contrasted with 'last'.

Reproducing colour patterns and carrying out instructions can involve 'make the *first* bead *red,* the *second* bead *blue* and the *third green*' and 'turn over the *second* card'.

31   Adding

Many of the addition facts in this section of work have already been met by the pupil and so will be revision for him. New facts are $5 + 1$, $4 + 2$, $5 + 2$, $3 + 3$, $4 + 4$, $5 + 5$.

Game

The children could play a game of 'doubles'. Two children play using a dice marked with 0 to 5 and cubes (or counters). Each child has ten cubes to begin. A player uses a throw of the dice to indicate how many cubes he must place in the centre of the table. The other child must match this number with his cubes. If the player can name the correct number of cubes now in the centre of the table he adds them to his collection; if he cannot give the correct sum, his opponent collects the cubes. If a player uses all his cubes he must retire from the game leaving the other player the winner, otherwise the player with the greater number of cubes is the winner. The children can find the greater number by matching if it is beyond their counting ability.

32 Subtracting

Many of the subtraction facts will also have been met before but $6 - 1$, $7 - 2$ and $6 - 2$ are likely to be new. These should be linked to concrete materials, e.g. toy cars can be used like this: 'Park 6 cars. Drive 1 away. How many are left?' The number line should also be used for subtraction activities, e.g. 'Take 7 steps forward. Step back 2. Where are you?'

Games

Games can be made up using a spinner marked with numerals 1 to 10. Here is an example of a 'Subtract 1' game. Each player is given a set of numeral cards for 0 to 9. These are placed face up in a row in front of him. The player uses the spinner and then subtracts 1 from the indicated number. To record the answer he turns over the appropriate numeral card. If a child cannot record the answer because he has already turned over that card, the next player is asked to do so (or the next and so on). The first player with all his cards turned over is the winner.

33 Addition 'stories' of six, seven, eight, nine and ten

The stories of six to ten have been left until now because the pupil will be involved in the full range of numbers 0 to 10. Once again many of the addition facts are not new; however twenty-seven of them are:

2 + 4	4 + 3	5 + 3	6 + 3	7 + 3
1 + 5	3 + 4	3 + 5	5 + 4	6 + 4
0 + 6	2 + 5	2 + 6	4 + 5	4 + 6
	1 + 6	1 + 7	3 + 6	3 + 7
	0 + 7	0 + 8	2 + 7	2 + 8
			1 + 8	1 + 9
			0 + 9	0 + 10

The facts in the boxed section have been met by the pupil in reverse order e.g. $4 + 2$, $5 + 1$, $6 + 0$. This can be brought to the child's notice. However, the steps from concrete materials to the abstract should be made slowly and repeated practice of these facts should be given in worksheet examples.

A pattern can be built up with pegs on pegboard for each story, e.g. the story of seven could be shown using two colours of pegs like this:

```
0 0 0 0 0 0 0    7 + 0
0 0 0 0 0 0 ●    6 + 1
0 0 0 0 0 ● ●    5 + 2
0 0 0 0 ● ● ●    4 + 3
0 0 0 ● ● ● ●    3 + 4
0 0 ● ● ● ● ●    2 + 5
0 ● ● ● ● ● ●    1 + 6
● ● ● ● ● ● ●    0 + 7
```

The number balance can also be used. One weight is attached to the 7 on the right-hand side and this is balanced by as many combinations of two numbers on the left-hand side as possible.

Work with the number balance can be linked to a recording format like this so that the child knows exactly what to do.

Story of 7

$$5 + 2$$

☐ + ☐

☐ + ☐

☐ + ☐

☐ + ☐

☐ + ☐

He can be shown how to place the weights for the first example and see the 7 balanced. How many other 'stories' can be found are indicated by the boxes.

Game

A game suitable for this stage is a form of the card game Pelmanism. A pack of numeral cards is prepared for each story. The 'Story of seven' would require two cards with each of these numerals 0, 1, 2, 3, 4, 5, 6, 7. (The 'Story of eight' would use two cards of each numeral from 0 to 8.) The cards are shuffled and then laid out face down, e.g. four rows and four columns. Each player turns over two cards. If these numbers add to seven (or eight etc) they are claimed by the player, if not they are turned face down again. For some children a simpler version is to lay out cards marked 0 to 7 on the top row, face up, and set out a second row of shuffled cards below these.

The child points to one card on the top row and says, for example, 'Six and this make seven'. At 'this' he turns over any card of his choice from the lower row. If the cards give the required total of seven, the child collects both cards, if not the chosen card is turned face down again. The player to win most cards is the winner.

34   Subtraction stories of six, seven, eight, nine and ten

This section of work again brings a large number of new bonds to the child's notice. Here they are—twenty-five of them.

$6 - 3$	$7 - 3$	$8 - 3$	$9 - 3$	$10 - 3$
$6 - 4$	$7 - 4$	$8 - 4$	$9 - 4$	$10 - 4$
$6 - 5$	$7 - 5$	$8 - 5$	$9 - 5$	$10 - 5$
	$7 - 6$	$8 - 6$	$9 - 6$	$10 - 6$
		$8 - 7$	$9 - 7$	$10 - 7$
			$9 - 8$	$10 - 8$
				$10 - 9$

Work with a variety of concrete materials is recommended. The story of eight could be carried out by the child pretending to be putting zoo animals in cages—the eight animals could be represented by plastic shapes or blocks. The child, as keeper, says, 'I have eight animals. One in a cage leaves seven animals. I have eight animals. Two in cages leave six animals' etc. The child could also be a postman with a bundle of letters to deliver. The story of six becomes, 'I have six letters. One for Mrs Jones leaves five to deliver. I had six letters. One for Mrs Jones, one for Mrs Brown leaves four to deliver' etc. The children, of course, love any repetition and the deliveries could be made using a row of houses or a row of children.

Variety makes practice examples more fun. A workcard (page 54) could be completed by a set of numeral cards (0 to 7) being placed in the correct position.

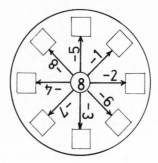

The subtraction 'merry-go-rounds' are ideal for all the stories. For the slowest children the numbers to be subtracted would be better ordered in a clockwise direction.

35   Complementary addition

Complementary addition examples are presented to the child as 'and how many more make'. This is, of course, another aspect of subtraction. This new way of looking at a situation may be a little difficult for the child. Easy steps, like these, might be followed: 'Show me seven blocks. I'll give you one block. How many blocks do you have now? Yes, seven and one make eight. Show me three blocks. How many blocks must I give you so that you have four blocks? Three and how many make four?'

Taking steps on the number line is helpful for this type of example: 'Go to 5 on the number line. How many steps must you take to get to 6?'

Some children may be able to cope with examples where the first number is one e.g. 'one and how many make four?', but these are more difficult.

36   Checking known addition and subtraction facts

Worksheet pages of examples of both addition and subtraction facts should be completed. However, games involving the addition or subtraction of two numbers readily show whether a child can find these answers and with how much facility.

Game
Use a track like that for Snakes and Ladders and allow the player's move to be determined by the sum of the numbers on the top faces of two dice. The dice used should be one of these combinations:

each marked with 0 to 5
one marked 1 to 6, the other 0 to 4 plus an extra 0
one marked 3 to 8, the other with 0, 1, 2 on each of two faces.

The same track and combinations of dice may be used for a subtraction version of the game. However, if a move is indicated by the subtraction of the smaller number from the larger, it will be a much slower game and so a smaller track might be advisable. Two dice each marked with 5 to 10 can also be used, or one of these with any other dice is also suitable for the subtraction version. The dice are easily made by writing numerals on the faces of cubes.

37   Adding more than two numbers
The union of three sets is best *not* introduced as laying out the three sets and then combining the members in one new set. The child may be able to cope with three numbers when they are represented by concrete materials but in the abstract he can only deal with two at a time. Addition is a binary operation i.e. two numbers are involved. So it is advisable to make the use of concrete materials a two-step process. Combine two sets, find the answer, and then link this to the third set, e.g. 3 + 2 + 4

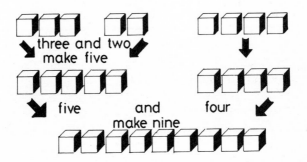

Recording of these examples might be tackled in these formats:

🍎 🍎 + 🍎 🍎 + 🍎   2 + 3 + 1   2

= 2 + 3 + 🍎   = ☐ + 1   + 3
                                          ———
= 5 + 1   = ☐   ☐

= 6   + 1

The more formal presentation of 2 + 3 + 1, either horizontal or vertical, is probably best left till later for some children, especially the slow learners.

38   Repeated addition patterns

Activities with concrete materials building up patterns of twos (threes and fours) are a first introduction to multiplication, but the child need not be made aware of this at the moment. Towers of twos can be made and results recorded orally as 'one two is two; two twos are four; three twos are six; four twos are eight and five twos are ten'. 'Two-steps' can be taken on the number line. The number balance can be used by placing weights on the 2 on the left-hand side and finding the answer on the right-hand side.

Pattern of threes

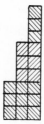

Patterns of three and of four can be built up in the same way. Formal recording should not be used at this stage.

39   Another early multiplication pattern

Blocks, the number line and the number balance can be used to establish these patterns.

Two ones   0●   Three ones   0●●
Two twos   00●●   Three twos   000●●●
Two threes 000●●●   Three threes 000●●●●●●
Two fours   00000●●●
Two fives   000000●●●●

Pattern of triples

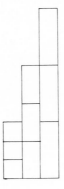

These patterns can also be built up pictorially, using gummed shapes and by colouring squares.

40   Equal sharing
Sharing is an activity a child indulges in before relating it to number work, for example when he shares sweets with his companions. Representations of sweets, biscuits and cakes should be shared between two dolls (or plates) and amongst three and four. The situations should be structured so that there is no remainder. The child will share 'one to you, one to you' and so on. This is all that is required at present.

41   Repeated subtraction
Equal sharing is one aspect of division and repeated subtraction is the other. Here the child is required to partition a set into subsets of a given cardinality by being asked, for example, 'How many threes are in six?' This can be shown by building 'three-towers' or laying out an array of threes. Again, the activities should be structured so that there is no remainder.

FRACTIONS
The pupil should be able to:
42   recognize unequal and equal parts
43   understand a whole as an undivided object
44   recognize, match and create halves.

42   Unequal and equal parts

If the children have not already met and played with jigsaw puzzles, this is a good time to introduce them. The puzzles should consist of only a few pieces. As the child tries to build up the picture, language referring to the bits or parts can be included: 'What can you see on the large part? Will this small part fit here?'

Home-made puzzles of pictures glued on card, polystyrene or board can be used to emphasize equal and unequal parts. Recognition of equal parts can come from finding pieces which fit exactly on top of each other, e.g.

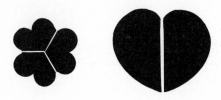

These 'flowers' could be made up with equal pieces.

43   A whole

Some understanding of this concept might arise from incidents in the home or classroom. A broken vase is repaired and made whole again. The child is given not a part of but a whole cake to share among his friends. Jigsaws are made into a whole picture.

The divided pictures mentioned in the preceding section involve language like 'Put these parts together to make a whole flower'.

44   Halves

The halves that a child meets in everyday life do little to help his understanding of a half as one of two equal parts. A half-pound of butter, a half-pint of milk, a half-penny, all appear to be complete objects, not part of anything.

Activities to aid his understanding should concentrate on a whole being divided into two parts, and the possibility of these being equal parts.

Many slabs of chocolate are made so that they break easily into two equal parts. These are better illustrations of halves than trying to divide equally apples and tarts.

Let the child select a half to match the one shown on a workcard from a selection of parts. One half of the drawings can be coloured.

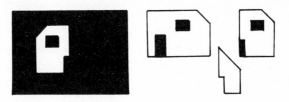

The pupil can find two rods which fit together to make up the red, the pink, the light green, the tan and the orange Cuisenaire rod, and identify one of these as one half of each rod.

MONEY
The pupil should be able to:
45 recognize the one-penny, two-pence, five-pence and ten-pence coins
46 recognize, match to coins, and record the amounts 1p, 2p, 5p, 10p where p represents the word pence
47 show, recognize and record amounts 1p to 10p in one-penny coins
48 add 1p, add 2p
49 take away 1p, take away 2p
50 match these equivalent values:
    one two-pence coin and two one-penny coins
    one five-pence coin and five one-penny coins.

45   Coin recognition
Money activities should be closely linked to the child's progress in number. The coin which will mainly be used at this stage is the one penny. The child should identify a one-penny coin from a box of plastic coins. The size of the coin, the design, the numeral and the words 'new penny' on the face of the coin should be discussed. The child can then find a set of these one-penny coins from the box. As well as sorting, the child can carry out a matching activity based on size. Outlines, into which two-pence, one-pence and half-pence coins can be fitted, should be drawn on a card. The child can find which outline best fits the one-penny coin and then match a one-pence coin to each outline of this size. Later in the school session, sorting and matching activities can be carried out for the two-pence, five-pence and ten-pence coins.

46   Money notation
As each coin is introduced, the appropriate recording should follow. The

letter p is used as a short form of the word pence.

Shopping could be based initially on a '1p tray'. This can consist of representations of sweets, e.g. toffees made by twisting paper around a crumpled piece of newspaper, biscuits made from rolled and glued foam sheet, sweets made from blobs of Polyfilla. The tray should be labelled clearly with the price 1p.

One child can be shopkeeper, while the others are customers provided with one-penny coins to exchange for goods.

Cards showing a picture of one-penny, two-pence, five-pence and ten-pence coins can be made up using gummed printed coins, a rubber coin stamp or by drawing. These can be matched to cards marked with 1p, 2p, 5p and 10p.

To give practice in recording these values, the child could be asked to identify pictures of coins and write the 'name' beside each. He could also write labels for the items in the one-penny tray (and other trays e.g. 2p, 5p).

Game
A pack of these cards could be used for a game of Snap. 'Snap' can be called when two one-penny coin pictures, two 1p cards or one picture and one 1p card, come next to each other.

47   Amounts expressed in one-penny coins
The child has to be able to show and to recognize the value of sets of one-penny coins.

The child should be given some purses. Inside each there are different numbers of one-penny coins. The child records the amount on a piece of paper and inserts this into the purse, placing the coins back in the coin box. Another child, or the same one on another occasion, can be given the task of putting one-penny coins for the value indicated in each purse.

Track game
This track game is greatly enjoyed by the pupils and is ideal at this stage. Each pupil is given three one-penny coins. Some boxes on the track are empty; others contain a 1p coin (see opposite).

A player throws the dice and moves a counter along the track the required number of places. If there is a 1p coin in the cox, he collects it. If the player lands in a box where there is no coin, he must place one of his there. After all the players have crossed the finishing line, the one with the most one-penny coins is the winner.

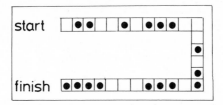

48   Adding 1p and 2p

Each child is given a box containing an equal number of one-penny coins (about 25 to 30) to play an 'adding 1p' game. A throw of the dice indicates to each player a number to which he must add 1 and then put coins for that value in the centre of the table. The first child with no coins left is the winner.

An 'adding 2p' game can use the same materials. The one-penny coins are placed in a pile in the centre of the table. The throw of the dice indicates the number to which the player should add 2. Coins for this value are claimed by the player. The winner is the player to claim the last coin from the centre of the table.

Worksheet examples can give the pupil extra practice of his number skills.

49   Subtracting 1p and 2p

This game is for four players. Each player begins with ten one-penny coins. A player throws the dice and gives the amount indicated to the player on his left. That player takes away 1p and passes the other coins, stating how many, to the player on his left. The first player with no coins left is the winner. A 'take away 2p' version of this game can also be played.

Worksheet examples like these can be used:

1   John has ⓵ ⓵ ⓵ ⓵ ☐

    He spends   ⓵ ☐

    He has left   ☐

2   take away 1p   take away 1p
    8p ──────────→ ☐ ──────────→ ☐

3		John	Bob	Dick	David
has		4p	7p	6p	9p
spends		−2p	−1p	−1p	−2p
has left		___	___	___	___

50   Equivalent values

The relationships between the coins are based on value, which is abstract and difficult for children at this stage to understand. Only simple examples relating the two-pence and the five-pence coins to one-penny coins should be investigated. At the shop, items in the 2p tray can be paid for either by two one-penny coins or by one two-pence coin. When the children shop give them a customer card and a purse of coins, e.g.

The child who has to buy the cake may have a purse with three one-penny coins in it. He finds the cake costs 2p. He pays with two of his one-penny coins. The pupil who is instructed to buy the chocolate finds he pays his 2p with one two-pence coin because his purse contains one two-pence coin and one penny coin.

Game

This is a game where children can exchange one-penny coins for five-pence coins. A box of one-penny and five-pence coins is required. A player throws the dice and collects the amount of one-penny coins indicated. Every time a player finds he has five one-penny coins he exchanges these for one five-pence coin. The first child to obtain four five-pence coins is the winner.

MEASURE

In *length*, the pupil should be able to:

51   describe and recognize objects in terms of linear measure e.g. long, short, tall, small, high, low

52   compare two lengths by placing them side by side to find the longer, the shorter, the taller etc

53   conserve length i.e. realize that matched lengths do not change when one or both lengths are moved into another position.

In *volume*, the pupil should be able to:

54   describe and recognize that containers can be full or empty, can hold more or hold less, can hold as much as.

In *area*, the pupil should be able to:

55   recognize and cover a surface

56   compare two surfaces by placing one on another.

In *weight*, the pupil should be able to:

57   describe and recognize objects in terms of weight e.g. heavy, light

58   use a simple balance to compare objects as heavy, light, balanced.

In *time*, the pupil should be able to:

59   order events e.g. getting-up time, breakfast time, going-to-school time; putting on a shirt, a tie, a jacket.

51   Basic concepts of length

A young child tends to label objects as 'big', whether he is referring to length, overall size or weight. A vocabulary which is more discriminating has to be introduced. Words like 'long', 'tall', 'small' and 'high' do not have much meaning unless they are used in a comparative situation, e.g. longer than my arm. However, for the child these words are a first step into the world of linear measure. When the child does begin to use these words, it is usually with himself as the object of comparison e.g. 'the boy is tall' means 'the boy is taller than I am'. Objects are called 'long' if the child has to stretch out his arms to hold them; they are 'high' if the child has to stand on tiptoe to try to reach them.

It is interesting to realize the variety of words we use to describe length and to consider how much convention has made one term correct in one context and seem wrong in another. The ladder is said to be 'long' even when it is placed against a tall building. 'The pencil is thick', 'the road is wide' and 'the lady is fat' are all expressions of width. Art work gives opportunities for the child to hear and use the language of length as he draws pictures and makes models. Structured activities should also be used to introduce a specific word, e.g. to establish 'long' the pupil can make a long necklace of beads and a long snake of Plasticine as well as find a long stick and a long piece of ribbon. When telling a story, the teacher can incorporate the word she wishes the children to know better, e.g. 'Willie was a long, long worm. When he was happy he rippled all along his body, all the way from his head to the tip of his tail. He loved to make long, long tunnels down into the earth.'

52   Comparison of two lengths

Objects which the child can stand on the table in front of him are probably the easiest for him to compare in order to find the taller. Cartons and bottles are excellent objects for this activity. Out of doors, lamp-posts, trees, traffic signs and buildings can be looked at. Comparison between the children themselves is made more interesting if a tall child and a small one lie down on newspaper (or wrapping paper) so that an outline of their bodies can be made. These outlines can be cut out and 'stood' against the wall so that the difference in height can be seen clearly and commented upon. To find the longer of two sticks or pieces of ribbon the child should be taught to align them at one end by placing the ends, against, for example, the edge of the table or holding them in their fingers.

The written form of the length words can be introduced to the child through the use of flash cards which can be used to label the results of his comparison activities.

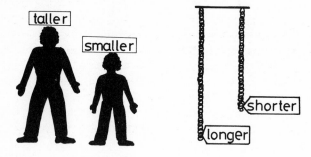

Game

Two children can play a game to find the longer 'necklace'. Each child throws a dice. The child whose dice shows the greater number collects a bead from a box. The beads are threaded or 'popped' together and after a specific time the child with the longer length of beads is the winner.

53   Conservation of length

In the comparison work suggested in the last section each activity was structured so that the child had only to consider one aspect of the total situation.

This allows the child to make the comparison whether or not he has secured the concept of the conservation of length. Before proceeding to less structured examples, it is advisable to test the pupil's understanding of length as suggested in 'The learner'.

54   The beginning of volume
Play with sand or at the water bath can give pupils the opportunity of filling and emptying bottles and containers. In describing his activities, the child can become familiar with words like fill, full, empty, pour, holds more, holds less and holds as much as.

It is interesting to note difficulties of interpretation in pouring activities. For example, the pupil has two containers, one large and one small. The child fills the larger container with water. He then pours the water from the larger into the smaller container until it is full. He now has one small container which is full and one large one with only a little water. If the pupil is asked at this point 'Which holds more?', he will point to the small container and say 'This one'. This question is inappropriate to the task. The child should be asked to consider which container will hold more orange juice for him to drink. He should look at both containers full of water before he empties the smaller and then pours from the larger.

55   The beginning of area
The early concepts of area, like those of volume, are not easy for the pupil. Activities emphasizing the nature of a surface can, however, emerge from art work and play. The child is encouraged to paint over the surface of the paper, to cover the table with the tablecloth and spread butter over a slice of bread.

56   Comparison of surfaces
As the child plays in the home corner of the classroom, he compares surface areas. He chooses which sheet will cover the bed, which tablecloth will be suitable when setting out the table for tea, and which sheet of coloured paper will cover the lid of a box. All that should be required at this stage is that the pupil should realize that a surface is something which he can move his hand over, and that he can find that one surface may be greater or less than another.

57   Basic concepts of weight
'Heavy' is introduced to the child as a more discriminating term than big. As far as the young child is concerned objects which are big are heavy.

His inability to pick up an object may be due to either its size or its weight so he tends to assume that these qualities are the same. In early activities nothing is to be gained in challenging this assumption. Let 'heavy' objects be large and 'light' ones small.

58   Using a balance

It is difficult to estimate the weight of an object held in the hand because of other considerations, e.g. the amount of surface area in contact with the hand. An instrument is required to combine the child's senses of seeing and feeling. A simple balance can be used. Suppliers offer a large selection of these but choice should be based on usefulness to the child. The 'arm' type allows the child to see clearly any movement up or down yet it often has great limitation as to the size of object which can be suspended in the small pan. Fortunately some of the latest designs overcome this problem.

The chosen pairs for balancing should initially be well contrasted examples of heavy and light. The child can pick up the two objects, feel the difference in weight and then see what happens to the balance pan on which the heavy object has been placed. A flash card can be used to label each side of the balance. Later it should be possible to include pairs of parcels between which it is more difficult to discriminate and possibly to have at least one or two pairs which balance each other.

A seesaw in the playground allows the child to see his classmates compared by weight. He can also experiment with his own seesaw, made from a ruler and a matchbox, to discover whether his rubber is 'heavy' when compared with his pencil sharpener.

59   Sequence of events

At home the child is given a pattern of daily and weekly happenings. The school should build on this and help establish some concepts of time. Through discussion the pupil realizes that some events happen *before* others, while some happen *after* others. This can be linked to activities such as dressing the doll, where the order of putting on garments is important; cooking, where a procedure of preparation is followed; and to games where a pattern of play is evolved. Drawings, where the child helps the teacher label each event with a sentence, can then be ordered by the pupil.

SHAPE
The pupil should be able to:

60   **show an awareness of 'inside' and 'outside' by using such terms to describe the position of an object in relation to others in the environment**

61   **extend this vocabulary of spatial awareness to include words such as in, under, on, beside, behind, underneath, in front of**

62   **recognize that a three-dimensional shape has surfaces and that these can either be flat or curved.**

60   Spatial awareness

Dienes and Golding (1967) suggest that the pupil might be introduced to three-dimensional shape through an exploration of surfaces:

> So, insides and outsides, holes, fronts, and backs and things of this kind, interest him. These are the sort of ideas which are termed in geometry 'topological' ones and here we must start.

As the child explores his environment, his awareness of space can be expressed in new vocabulary such as 'inside' and 'outside'. Instructions demand that he 'put the blocks inside the box', 'place the pennies inside the purse' and 'should stand outside the room and knock'.

Specific tasks can be given to the child to establish his understanding of inside and outside with reference to objects and to himself. The pupil can help to make number boxes. These are boxes labelled with a numeral on the outside and filled with the appropriate number of beads.

The pupil can describe the objects inside each room of the doll's house, and those outside in the garden, using either a model house or a picture of one.

When the pupils were carrying out sorting tasks, an awareness of regions probably emerged. Emphasis on members being inside and outside the boundary of the set, and why this is so, can be made, e.g. 'all the beads *inside* the ring have holes, and this bead *outside* has no hole'.

Game

Fun can emerge from a game of 'Follow the leader'. Here a small group of three or four children can follow one child who must describe the route he is taking. The activity can be confined to the classroom, the school or the playground: 'I am going *inside* the Wendy House; I am going *outside* to the corridor; I am going *inside* the cupboard.'

61   Positional vocabulary

'Inside' and 'outside' are just two terms which express an object's spatial relationship to other fixtures in the environment. The child meets other words as he receives or gives instruction, e.g. 'Put the blocks *beside* the pencils', 'Push the box *under* the table *in* the cupboard' and 'Stand *in front of* Jean and *behind* Robert'.

Game
The child's understanding of such positional vocabulary can be checked by playing a game with two objects such as a block and a box. The teacher gives the child an instruction, e.g. 'put the block *in front of* the box'. Then it is the child's turn to give an instruction to the teacher, e.g. 'Put the block *in* the box'. If the child's ability allows him to cope with a written vocabulary, a set of positional cards (on, in, behind, in front of, under, beside) can be made and the instruction is shown when the card is turned over.

Preparing and setting out an obstacle course either in the classroom, corridor or playground is excellent practice. The pupils set out boxes to be climbed over, cardboard 'tunnels' to be squeezed through, a table to be crawled under etc. Discussion of what has to be done can take place and then each child goes around the course describing what he is doing, e.g. 'I am climbing *on top of* the wooden box. I go *through* the hoop. I squeeze *behind* the book cupboard'.

62   Three-dimensional shapes
In spatial activities as well as in early measure work, the child has gained experience in handling three-dimensional shapes.

Opportunities should be made to emphasize the faces of such shapes. The pupil can help to make dice for games by writing numerals or drawing sets of dots on the faces of a variety of shapes.

These dice need to be picked up as the number on the face next to the table is the one used.

The child should be encouraged to experiment in building towers with shapes other than cubes and in making models of trains, vehicles, robots and monsters with a variety of cartons. As he begins to realize that sufaces are either flat or curved, the child can investigate whether or not a shape can roll. This consideration of how a shape rolls helps to focus attention on the curved surface, e.g. the cylinder rolls in a straight line, the cone or cream tub (a fustrum of a cone) rolls in a circle, the sphere can spin on the point of contact, and the ovoid (egg) wobbles along.

PICTORIAL REPRESENTATION
The pupil should be able to:
63   construct and interpret simple data in a display of three-dimensional objects.

63   Pictorial representation
The pupil has been making and looking at pictorial representation in all aspects of the work in Stage 1. However, a new emphasis can be given to such work if the child sees such representations as telling 'stories' about 'special' sets. Here is just one example presented in a variety of ways. The special set in this instance is a selection of different biscuits.

Sorting
Each child in a group chooses his favourite biscuit. The favourites and the other biscuits can be displayed like this:

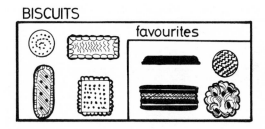

   The child should realize that the display is only meaningful if labels are shown to tell the 'story'. The pupils should look at the displays made by other groups and discuss if these are the same, or different, and in what way.

Matching
Several children may like the same kind of biscuit. This data may be displayed in a mapping diagram. Each child should make a label of his name and attach this to a length of string. A display can be formed like this:

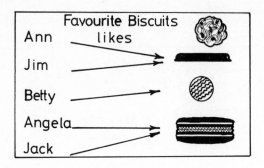

Favourite biscuits

Number

Biscuits		
Ann	Betty	altogether
		4
		4
		4
		4

How many biscuits?

Kit Kat

2   biscuits

4   biscuits

6   biscuits

8   biscuits

Measure

Shape

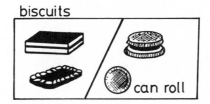

A beginning can also be made in block graphs. If the objects are going to be displayed for easy quantitative comparison, certain teaching points have to be made. Each set should be built up from a vertical or horizontal 'starting line' and each member of the sets should occupy an equal area. These points are easily made by structuring the situation perhaps like this:

Each child chooses his favourite biscuit and places this on a 'plate'. The plates are lined up at the start and placed next to each other with no gaps. The rows of plates can be labelled either with the empty biscuit packet or by a flash card.

This type of simple three-dimensional block graph can be made with sweets, plastic shapes to represent pet animals, toy vehicles to represent the type of traffic passing the school gate etc.

A discussion should be based on the display to expand the child's interpretation of the data. Questions along these lines can help structure such a discussion:

Are there more crunchies or mallows?
Which biscuits do pupils like more than mallows?
Which biscuit do most children like?
Which biscuit do fewest children like?
How many more children like fingers than mallows?
How many children have shown their favourite biscuit?

Questions are based on qualitative (more, less, as many as) comparisons as well as quantitative (how many more or less).

The comparison of two sets to find more or less is likely to give difficulty to the slow learner but this type of activity gives another opportunity for members to be matched and the difference between the sets highlighted so that another step towards understanding might be taken.

At this stage number work in the discussion of a display should be within the range zero to ten.

References
DIENES, Z.T. and GOLDING, E.W. (1967) *The First Years in Mathematics Part 3: Exploration of Space and Practical Measurement* ESA
FLETCHER, H. (1970) *Mathematics for Schools* Addison-Wesley

A series of mathematics workbooks which might be used to help the pupil achieve the objectives listed in Stage 1 is Aileen Duncan's *Numbers and Words* (Books 1-4), published by Ward Lock Educational.

STAGE 2

Number
In Stage 2 the range of numbers with which the learner calculates is extended to twenty. This number work is separated into two parts.

1 Numbers 10 to 19
This part is concerned with recognition of sets, matching these to the correct numerals and reproducing the numerals. These numbers are then seen as one ten and a number of units. This early introduction to place value makes it easier for the learner to associate the number facts in the range zero to ten with these 'new' numbers. After addition and subtraction of one and of two, the learner is introduced to the story of nineteen. The number bonds for nineteen are all based on known facts. This unusual order, nineteen to sixteen, leaves the largest amount of new work till later when the pupil is more able to learn it.

2 Numerals 0 to 20
This part finds the pupil meeting the number stories for fifteen to eleven. The number facts for eleven are the most difficult as the pupil has not previously met any of them. Complementary addition is introduced and there are some simple multiplication and division activities.

More games are included to give practice in the increasing amount of number facts which the pupil has to know.

Fractions
Halves are revised and quarters are introduced.

Money
Money activities are linked to the addition, subtraction and complementary addition experienced in number. It is suggested that these are linked to the appropriate number sections in the order of teaching, e.g. section 36 could follow sections 9 and 10; section 38 could come after section 24.

Measure
Qualitative comparisons are made in length, volume, area and weight activities. In length, the pupil progresses to quantitative work using arbitrary standards. Days of the week and telling the time lead the pupil to a greater awareness of time.

Shape
In shape work, three-dimensional shapes are made in clay, investigated for similarities and differences of edges, faces and corners, and labelled as cubes, cylinders, cuboids, cones and spheres.

Pictorial representation
Pictographs are constructed and interpreted.

NUMBERS 10 TO 19
The pupil should be able to:
1   recognize, name and create sets with cardinalities of eleven to nineteen
2   recognize, name and match to the appropriate set, the numerals 11 to 19
3   reproduce the numerals 11 to 19
4   order sets with cardinalities of ten to nineteen
5   order number names and numerals 10 to 19
6   recognize and create the relationships of 'is greater than' and 'is less than' between sets, number names and numerals
7   show sets with cardinalities ten to nineteen grouped as tens and units
8   link the grouping into tens and units to place-value notation
9   add 1, add 2
10   take away 1, take away 2
11   partition sets of 19, 18, 17 and 16 to show addition bonds
12   partition sets of 19, 18, 17 and 16 to show subtraction bonds

1   Cardinality of sets eleven to nineteen
These numbers are well beyond the possibility of recognition so they must be introduced in the order from smallest to greatest so that the members can be counted. As large a variety of materials as possible should be used by the child to make sets of the required cardinality, e.g. he can build towers of Unifix blocks, make chains of beads, set out arrays of counters, make lines of pegs on pegboard, park toy cars, 'cage' plastic animals.

The pupil should also be able to recognize and name the cardinality of sets presented to him as a collection of objects, a picture or a drawing.

This work should not be rushed as the names of the numbers are either being met for the first time or being given a new understanding. It is possibly a good idea to concentrate on sets of cardinality eleven to fifteen, then consider the numerals 11 to 15. This can then be followed by emphasis on sets of sixteen to nineteen and the numerals 16 to 19.

2/3   Numerals 11 to 19
Collections of sets of a specific cardinality can be labelled with appropriate tags:

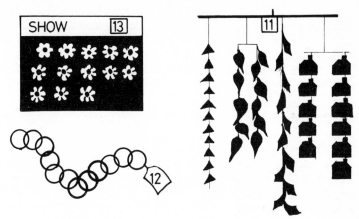

Domino cards can be used to match sets with numerals. (For ease of reference all domino diagrams have been set out as below. The actual cards would follow the traditional domino format.)

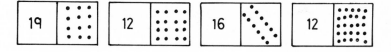

4/5   Ordering
The pupil can build towers of ten, eleven, twelve, thirteen etc to nineteen blocks and then set these out like a staircase.

Numerals can then be linked to each tower so that they too are ordered from smallest to greatest. The opportunity should be taken to extend the number line (see page 42) on the floor or along the wall. If the numerals are on cards the children can fix these in position in the correct order.

Emphasis should be laid on 'which number comes before' and 'which number comes after' so that order is established without the child always having to count from ten, or worse still, from 0.

6   Relationships

The teacher can lay out a set of counters (in the number range eleven to nineteen) and ask the child to show a set with more, or a set with less. This is most easily done by matching the given set and then adding extra counters to show more, or removing some to show less. The pupil can count his set and make a statement such as 'Fourteen is less than sixteen'.

Sorting exercises can be used to emphasize 'numbers greater than' and 'numbers less than'. Cards with the numerals 10 to 19 written on them can be sorted as shown in this diagram:

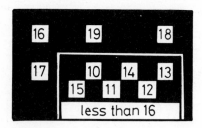

Arrow diagrams can be made. In the first diagram the child has drawn arrows to show the relationship 'is greater than' or he can show numerals in the blank boxes.

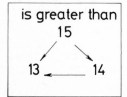
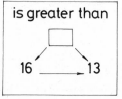
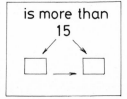

Game

A game is also possible at this time. Four sets of numeral cards (10 to 19) make up the playing pack. These cards are shuffled and each player is dealt six cards. Instruction cards stating 'more than 14', 'less than 17', 'greater than 11' etc are made and placed face down in a pile in the centre of the table. When an instruction is turned over, each player discards a number which fits the requirements. The first child who has been able to discard all his cards is the winner. If all the instruction cards are used before the game is finished, they should be shuffled and placed face down again so that play can continue.

7   Tens and units

It is difficult for the pupil to progress from counting to grouping in activities with sets of cardinalities eleven to nineteen, so it would be advantageous at this stage in the development of number to introduce a structured number material, e.g. cubes used as units and rods which can be matched by ten cubes used as tens. When the child first meets any new material he should have the opportunity of playing with it as he wishes. After this introduction he will then be ready to learn to use the material as the teacher suggests.

The child will require practice in matching ten units to one ten. This can be achieved through a variety of activities. 'Mister' cards can be made, each of which has a drawing of a head with a hat on. Ten unit-cubes fit along the brim of the hat and each card is labelled by a numeral in the range ten to nineteen. The appropriate number of unit cubes are used to fill squares representing the eyes, mouth, ears and nose:

The pupils can fill the squares either from the throw of a dice in a game or by working on their own. When the hat brim is filled, they exchange the ten units for one ten which also fits the brim.

If a sequence of cards has been filled these can be ordered and the child should also be encouraged to comment on each card, e.g. 'Mr 13 has one ten and three units'.

The children could be given a bag of units, any number in the range ten to nineteen, to match for a ten and then say how many are in the bag. Slow learners tend to count the units, count ten units for one ten and then count the total number again and so after some practice, it is useful to introduce an unmarked 'ten', e.g. the orange Cuisenaire rod, thus encouraging the child to match rather than to count when exchanging the units for the ten and thus to take a step nearer recognition of the cardinality of the set by saying 'ten, eleven, twelve', rather than by counting from 'one'.

8   Place-value notation

The child can build a staircase of units from one to nine. Beside this another staircase of tens and units can be built to show eleven to nineteen and these staircases can then be compared to see what is the same and what is different. The staircases could be labelled with numeral cards and these also compared for likenesses and differences.

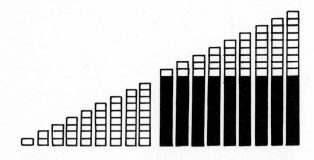

The pupil should be aware that:

1   sets of units of the same cardinality appear in the same order in each staircase
2   these sets of units are represented by the same numeral in both staircases
3   the one ten is recorded separately
4   the units digit occurs on the right-hand side of a number, and the tens digit to the left of this.

Now is a suitable time to introduce a 'notation card'. This can be a sheet of A4 size card (or paper) marked out as shown:

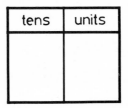

The pupil uses this card as a background for the ten and unit pieces when representing a number. Practice should be given in placing pieces on the card to represent numbers and in recognizing which number a display of pieces represents, e.g. one ten and three units are thirteen:

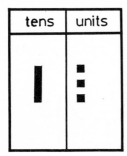 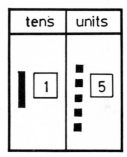

The link can be made with numerals by placing the appropriate numeral card beside the pieces.

9 Adding

It is necessary to revise the following number bonds before proceeding to the new work of this section: 0 + 1, 1 + 1, 2 + 1, 3 + 1, 4 + 1, 5 + 1, 6 + 1, 7+ 1, 8 + 1, 0 + 2, 1+ 2, 2 + 2, 3 + 2, 4 + 2, 5 + 2, 6 + 2, 7 + 2.

Revision can be carried out using the notation card to establish a pattern of laying out the pieces for addition.

When using the notation card, the pieces which represent the numbers are laid one below the other, e.g. 5 + 2 would be shown like this:

The units are collected together and placed in the answer area at the foot of the card. The pupil explains what he is doing with words, such as 'five units and two units are seven units'. Because of the introduction of the notation card and the cubes, the pupil may count to find the answer. After some practice the teacher can point out that the answer is one which the pupil knows and that the pupil can probably say the answer without counting.

The pupil can now tackle these numbers bonds: 10 + 1, 11 + 1, 12 + 1, 13 + 1, 14 + 1, 15 + 1, 16 + 1, 17 + 1, 18 + 1; 10 + 2, 11 + 2, 12 + 2, 13 + 2, 14 + 2, 15 + 2, 16 + 2, 17 + 2. Use of the number pieces will emphasize the relationship of these new bonds with those just revised.

Using the notation card, the pupil can lay out pieces to represent a number from ten to eighteen. One unit is placed below this number. The two sets of units are drawn together and placed in the answer area. The ten is also brought down to the answer space. The child should build up a language to explain what he is doing, such as 'three units and one unit are four units, one ten and no tens are one ten, one ten and four units are fourteen' (see opposite).

Again the slower pupils are likely to fall back to counting in order to find the answer of four units. In time, encourage the pupil to relate these additions to the bonds already known to him so that recognition of the answer replaces counting.

Addition of two units can be tackled in the same way, setting out a number from ten to seventeen and then the two units below that. When

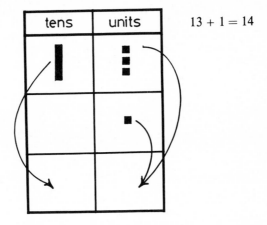

$13 + 1 = 14$

first recording these sums, use a horizontal format, e.g. $14 \xrightarrow{+2} 16$ and $14 + 2 = 16$. This allows the pupil to relate the unit digits to the language pattern established while using the number pieces. When a vertical setting of the calculation is used, the habit of adding from the top digit downwards should be adopted to keep the pattern consistent.

No exchange of ten units for one ten is brought into the calculations at this time.

10   Subtracting

The number facts to be dealt with in this section of the work are: $19 - 1$, $18 - 1$, $17 - 1$, $16 - 1$, $15 - 1$, $14 - 1$, $13 - 1$, $12 - 1$, $11 - 1$; $19 - 2$, $18 - 2$, $17 - 2$, $16 - 2$, $15 - 2$, $14 - 2$, $13 - 2$, $12 - 2$. The pupil will find these bonds easier if revision of subtracting 1 and of subtracting 2 is carried out with the numbers one to ten. Again, the notation card and number pieces can be used and this work could be followed by a game.

When using the notation card and the pieces only the larger number is shown, e.g. in 7–1, seven units are shown on the card, one unit is then removed and put at the side of the card while the other units are transferred to the answer area: 'I have seven units. I take away one unit and six units are left' (see p. 82, top).

When the pupil is ready to carry out subtraction of one and of two in the range of numbers ten to nineteen, the number pieces should be used. The calculation 15–2 would be worked like this: 'Fifteen is one ten and five units. I have five units. I take away two units and three units are left. I have one ten. I don't take away any tens so one ten is left. One ten and three units are thirteen' (see p. 82, middle).

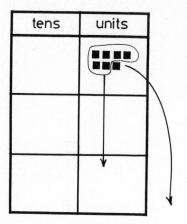

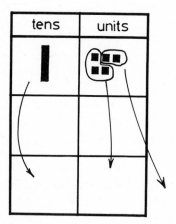

This pattern of language can be used in all future subtraction and provides the child with a framework when he carries out calculations without the use of materials.

The pupil can be shown that if the units which have been subtracted are added to the answer, the original number is obtained. This is a means of checking the calculation.

When recording these calculations it is again probably easier to use a horizontal setting, e.g. $15 \xrightarrow{-2} 13$ and $15 - 2 = 13$, followed by the vertical one. A consistent pattern of working will help the child in the later stage to avoid subtracting the numbers in the wrong order.

11   Addition stories for nineteen, eighteen, seventeen and sixteen

Revision of the addition stories for nine, eight, seven and six would be helpful. Given nine unit-cubes, the pupil could form his own 'sums' on the notation card and record each one.

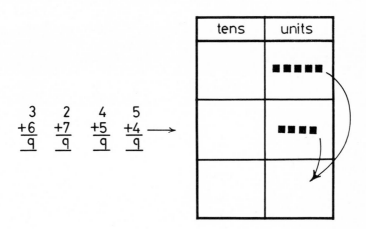

$$\begin{array}{cccc} 3 & 2 & 4 & 5 \\ +6 & +7 & +5 & +4 \\ \hline 9 & 9 & 9 & 9 \end{array}$$

The story of nineteen is mentioned first rather than the story of eleven because the addition facts for nineteen are the easiest in the range of numbers eleven to nineteen because *all* the unit bonds have already been met, while in the facts for eleven only two have been previously encountered i.e. 0 + 1 and 1 + 0.

The pupil can be given a notation card, one ten and nine unit-pieces and encouraged to construct and record his own stories for nineteen. He will find *some* of these facts: 19 + 0, 17 + 2, 16 + 3, 15 + 4, 14 + 5, 13 + 6, 12 + 7, 11 + 8, 10 + 9, 9 + 10, 8 + 11, 7 + 12, 6 + 13, 5 + 14, 4 + 15, 3 + 16, 2 + 17, 1 + 18, 0 + 19.

In the story of eighteen the child meets one new number bond, 9 + 9. There are two new facts, 9 + 8 and 8 + 9, in the story of seventeen and three new facts, 9 + 7, 8 + 8 and 7 +9, in the story of sixteen. These number facts are not only new but involve the exchange of units for a ten. Give the pupil the opportunity to find these facts when he is doing his stories but these bonds will require careful teaching. The pupil should learn to cope with the exchange process like this: 'Nine units and seven units are sixteen units. Sixteen units are one ten and six units'. When exchanging, the ten units should be matched rather than counted and the one ten placed in the tens answer place.

tens	units
	■■■■ ■■■■■
	■■■■ ■■■

12   Subtraction stories for nineteen, eighteen, seventeen and sixteen

Revision of the subtraction stories for nine, eight, seven and six will recall most of the subtraction bonds required for this section of work. The pupil cannot be left to find the subtraction stories for nineteen to sixteen on his own.

In the story of nineteen the following facts can be worked by the child from a workcard using the notation card and the number pieces (he sets out the larger number and removes the smaller to the side): $19 - 0$, $19 - 1$, $19 - 2$, $19 - 3$, $19 - 4$, $19 - 5$, $19 - 6$, $19 - 7$, $19 - 8$, $19 - 9$. The remainder of the facts for nineteen require an introduction by the

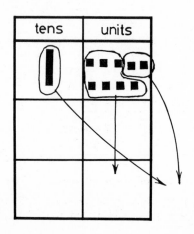

teacher because they involve the subtraction of units and of the ten, e.g. 19 − 12 should be worked in these steps: 'Nineteen is one ten and nine units. I have nine units. I take away two units leaving seven units. I have one ten. I take away one ten leaving no tens. Nineteen take away twelve leaves seven'.

In the stories of eighteen, seventeen and sixteen a new teaching point emerges. In the facts 18 − 9, 17 − 8, 17 − 9, 16 − 7, 16 − 8, and 16 − 9, the child does not have enough units to take away the required number and so must be introduced to a method of obtaining more units. The method here is decomposition. The example 17 − 8 would be worked like this: 'Seventeen is one ten and seven units. I have seven units. I want to take away eight units but I cannot.

tens	units
I	■ ■ ■ ■ ■ ■ ■

Exchange one ten for ten units. I have seventeen units.

tens	units
	■ ■ ■ ■ ■ ■ ■ ■ ■ ■ ■ ■ ■ ■ ■ ■ ■

'I take away eight units and leave nine units. Seventeen take away eight leaves nine'.

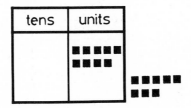

When the child performs the exchange, the ten should be put back in the box of pieces and not laid at the side of the notation cards thus avoiding confusion with pieces which have been subtracted. This training in good working habits is essential with the slow learner and will be to his advantage later on.

The pupil should be given practice in the addition and subtraction bonds of this section by being asked to complete worksheets of examples including a variety of formats perhaps like these:

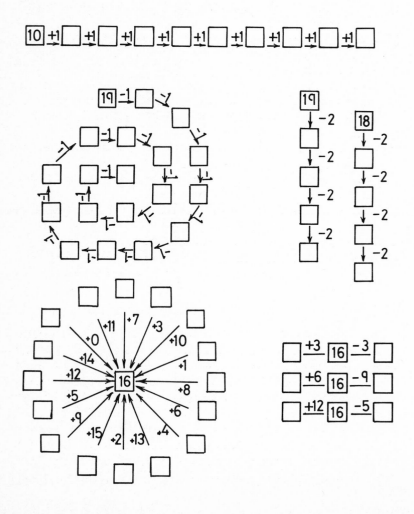

NUMBERS 0 TO 20
The pupil should be able to:

13   recognize, name and create a set of twenty
     recognize, name and match to the appropriate set the numeral 20
     reproduce the numeral 20
     show a set of twenty as two tens

14   order sets with cardinalities zero to twenty

15   order number names and numerals 0 to 20

16   recognize and create relationships of 'is greater than' and 'is less than' between sets, number names and numerals

17   recognize and create sequences e.g. 8, 9, 10, 11 and fourteen, thirteen, twelve

18   recognize and use ordinal number names fourth to twentieth

19   add and subtract zero

20   add 'doubles', e.g. 6 + 6

21   subtract 'doubles', e.g. 12 − 12

22   partition sets of 15, 14, 13, 12 and 11 to show addition stories

23   partition sets of 15, 14, 13, 12 and 11 to show subtraction stories

24   carry out complementary addition, e.g. $7 + \square = 18$

25   add or subtract any two numbers where these numbers and the answer is in the range zero to twenty

26   add three or four numbers where the sum is less than or equal to twenty

27   construct patterns of repeated addition, e.g. 3 + 3 + 3 + 3 + 3 or five threes

28   construct patterns of doubles, triples, e.g. 6 + 6 + 6 or three sixes

29   carry out equal sharing activities where there is no remainder

30   carry out repeated subtraction activities where there is no remainder.

13   Twenty

The number twenty can be introduced as the number which follows nineteen in the counting sequence. The pupils may also realize that this means it is 'one more than nineteen'. The classroom number line can have this number placed in position so that the pupils meet the numerical form 20. Labelling and other written exercises can provide the pupil with practice in reproducing the numeral.

   Representation of numbers such as seventeen, eighteen and nineteen with the structured number pieces should be revised before the pupil is presented with the problem of representing twenty. Some pupils may realize very quickly that twenty is shown as two tens but others may require help with the exchange of a second set of the units for another ten.

14   Ordering sets

Building staircases with Unifix blocks and especially with Cuisenaire rods not only orders sets of cardinalities one to twenty but again emphasizes that the pattern of rods from one to ten is repeated from eleven to twenty. This activity can also reinforce the fact that eleven is one ten and one unit, twelve is one ten and two units etc.

15   Ordering numerals

Making a picture of the 'staircase' one to twenty can be carried out by colouring squares on squared paper. Each stair can then be labelled by the appropriate numeral. A large version of this might be made on 5 cm squared paper by a group of pupils and displayed on the classroom wall. Zero can be included as the set of no blocks at the beginning of the staircase and labelled 0. Numeral cards for 0 to 20 can be shuffled and then given to a pupil for ordering in both ascending and descending order. Looking at this sequence of numerals the pupil can be asked to find the set of all the numbers which have a 1 ten, reinforcing yet again the grouping aspect of counting.

16   Relationships

As before, these relationships of 'more than' and 'less than' can be investigated with concrete materials, e.g. 'show me more counters than these', and in abstract exercises, e.g. 'circle all the numbers greater than 12: 4   16   6   14   0   20   18   8'.

17   Sequences

Let the pupils play an oral sequence game in a small group. One child chooses any number from one to nineteen. The other pupils must follow the number chosen by the first pupil in a counting sequence, e.g. 'nine, ten, eleven, twelve . . .'. The pupil who says 'twenty' ends the sequence and the next child chooses another number and this begins a new counting pattern. Other variations of this activity can be tried, e.g. counting in descending order when 'one' finishes the sequence; counting in 'twos' by saying the next number to yourself and the following one aloud. A card game to collect a sequence of three or four numeral cards can be played (a version of Rummy). Use numeral cards for 0 to 20.

18   Ordinal number names

The pupil has already been introduced to the names first, second and third. The names in this section are easier as they are mostly the number names with 'th' added: four*th*, fif*th*, six*th*, seven*th*, eigh*th*, nin*th*, ten*th*, eleven*th*, twelf*th*, thirteen*th*, fourteen*th*, fifteen*th*, sixteen*th*, seventeen*th*, eighteen*th*, nineteen*th*, twenti*eth*.

The pupil can carry out activities with a set of coloured counters, cards or pegs, e.g. 'make the fourteenth peg blue', 'turn over the twelfth card' and 'what colour is the sixteenth counter?'

19   Adding and subtracting zero

It was suggested earlier that adding and subtracting zero is not an easy concept for children to understand so this was introduced, but not given too much emphasis or consolidation. The number facts involving zero are still likely to present difficulty.

20   Adding doubles

The new number facts to be taught by the teacher and learned by the child in this section are $6 + 6$, $7 + 7$, $8 + 8$, $9 + 9$, $10 + 10$. The other 'doubles' facts involving the numbers 1 to 5 can also be revised at this time. Most children find these number facts easy and enjoy working with them.

21   Subtracting doubles

Zero, in this context is meaningful to most pupils. Practice of subtraction should include the subtraction of 'doubles' e.g. $13 - 13 = 0$.

22   Addition stories for fifteen, fourteen, thirteen, twelve and eleven

Revision of the addition stories for five, four, three and two is useful before beginning the new work of this section.

When using the number pieces to create stories for fifteen, the child should be involved in the bonds he has just revised, i.e.

$10 + 5$ as $10 + (0 + 5)$	$5 + 10$ as $(5 + 0) + 10$
$11 + 4$ as $10 + (1 + 4)$	$4 + 11$ as $(4 + 1) + 10$
$12 + 3$ as $10 + (2 + 3)$	$3 + 12$ as $(3 + 2) + 10$
$13 + 2$ as $10 + (3 + 2)$	$2 + 13$ as $(2 + 3) + 10$
$14 + 1$ as $10 + (4 + 1)$	$1 + 14$ as $(1 + 4) + 10$
$15 + 0$ as $10 + (5 + 0)$	$0 + 15$ as $(0 + 5) + 10$

The bond $13 + 2$ is illustrated with the number pieces on page 90. 'Three units and two units are five units. One ten and no tens are one ten. One ten and five units are fifteen'.

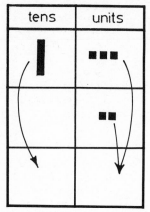

23 Subtraction stories for fifteen, fourteen, thirteen, twelve and eleven

The pupil should be asked to recall the subtraction bonds for the stories of five, four, three and two. The new bonds in the stories of fifteen are 9 + 6, 8 + 7, 7 + 8 and 6 + 9.

If the number pieces are used, the pupil will be required to exchange the units for one ten. Some pupils may have to be reminded of how to match the pieces to make the exchange. The new bonds for fourteen are 9 + 5, 8 + 6, 7 + 7, 6 + 8, 5 + 9; for thirteen they are 9 + 4, 8 + 5, 7 + 6, 6 + 7, 5 + 8, 4 + 9; for twelve they are 9 + 3, 8 + 4, 7 + 5, 6 + 6, 5 + 7, 4 + 8, 3 + 9; for eleven they are 9 + 2, 8 + 3, 7 + 4, 6 + 5, 5 + 6, 4 + 7, 3 + 8, 2 + 9.

The stories are suggested in the order fifteen to eleven because in that way the child meets the largest number of new bonds when he is most ready to cope with them.

The pupil will require much practice in these bonds, and this can be achieved through completing worksheet examples and playing games.

The subtraction stories for fifteen can be investigated by the child using the structured number pieces. Placing the pieces for fifteen on his notation board, he should remove and place at one side the pieces to represent the smaller number for these bonds, i.e. 15 − 5, 15 − 4, 15 − 3, 15 − 2, 15 − 1, 15 − 0. The pupil should then proceed to bonds involving the subtraction of one ten and a number of units, i.e. 15 − 15, 15 − 14, 15 − 13, 15 − 12, 15 − 11, 15 − 10. The most difficult set of examples are those involving the decomposition of the ten into ten units, i.e. 15 − 9, 15 − 8, 15 − 7, 15 − 6.

The language adopted by the teacher and the pupil should be as in section 12, the example 15−7 is worked like this: 'Fifteen is one ten and five units. I have five units. I want to take away seven units but I cannot.

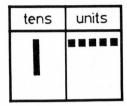

'I exchange one ten for ten units. I have fifteen units.

tens	units
	■ ■ ■ ■ ■ ■ ■ ■ ■ ■ ■ ■ ■ ■ ■

'I take away seven units and leave eight units. Fifteen take away seven leaves eight'.

tens	units
	■ ■ ■ ■ ■ ■ ■ ■

When exchanging the ten for the ten units the pupil should match rather than count the units. The exchanged ten should then be returned to the box of pieces and so be clearly removed from the calculation.

The pupil should tackle the subtraction bonds for the stories of fourteen, thirteen, twelve and eleven through the three types of examples suggested for the story of fifteen, i.e.

1   where the subtraction involves units only
2   where the subtraction involves tens and units with no exchange necessary
3   when the subtraction involves the decomposition of the ten.

Game
As well as practice examples the child should play games to help him

gain a familiarity with these number facts. Here is 'Subtraction Bingo', designed in this instance for the story of fourteen. The pupil who is the 'caller' is provided with a pack of numeral cards from 0 to 14 and an answer card for all the subtraction facts for fourteen. Each child is given a Bingo card marked with six numbers in the range zero to fourteen. The caller shuffles the numeral cards and places these face down in front of him. He turns over the top card and calls out this number. Each player subtracts this number from fourteen and if his Bingo card shows the answer he covers this number with a counter. The caller checks the correct answer from his answer card, sees that the players have covered the correct number and then proceeds to turn over another numeral card. The first player to cover the six numbers on his Bingo card is the winner.

24   Complementary addition

Many of the children will still find this aspect of subtraction difficult. If, perhaps, we link calculations to addition examples, they could have fun tackling 'twin sums'.

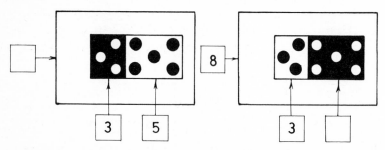

Examples, first with concrete materials and later in pictorial exercises, can illustrate addition then complementary addition, e.g. 'Three and five make eight. Three and how many make eight? Three and five make eight'. Later the twin 'sums' can be expressed as:

$$\boxed{10} + \boxed{5} = \boxed{} \qquad \boxed{8} + \boxed{6} = \boxed{}$$
$$\boxed{10} + \boxed{} = \boxed{15} \qquad \boxed{} + \boxed{6} = \boxed{14}$$

25   Checking known addition and subtraction facts

As well as working practice examples the pupils can be involved in a variety of games. Here are some which are easily made and played.

'Addition Bingo' game

Use two dice, one marked one to six, the other seven to twelve. Each child has a card marked with six numbers in the range eight to eighteen.

When constructing these, remember which combinations are possible, e.g. six combinations give the number 13 so it can be used frequently; 12 and 14 can be used almost as often; 10, 11, 15 and 16 less frequently and 8, 9, 17 and 18 only occasionally.

Each player throws the dice in turn and calls out the sum of their numbers. All players cover this answer with a counter if it appears on their Bingo card. The first player with the six numbers on his card covered is the winner.

'I can add' game

Each player is dealt six cards from a pack of numeral cards (four of each numeral 0 to 10). The remaining cards are placed face down in the centre of the table. A player decides on a number within the range four to twenty (slower pupils will benefit by being given a number, e.g. twelve, thirteen, ten) and it is his task to find three pairs of numbers which add to this chosen sum. Each player, in turn, can select the top card of the unseen pile or take the last card discarded by a player, discarding one card himself so that he never has more than six cards. As a player collects a pair, he places these cards face down in front of him. On collecting three pairs, he turns the cards over and shows them to the other players who check that all three pairs add to the same total. If the pairs are correct, this player wins the game.

Domino game

Make up your domino game with cards based on the combinations used in the original game, i.e. seven numbers each used eight times on twenty-eight cards each of which shows two numbers.

An addition version could be constructed using the numbers 7, 11, 12, 13, 15, 18 and 20, e.g.

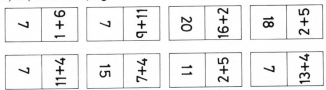

Note how the number 7 is used in these combinations (7,7) (7,20) (7,18) (7,15) (7,11) on the dominoes illustrated. Other cards with 7 are required to show (7,12) and (7,13) or (12,7) and (13,7).

The slower learner should play the game so that he is presented with a calculation and is seeking the answer. Placing the answer in position he is given a new calculation to do. It is much more difficult to be given an answer and asked to find a calculation which fits it.

26   Adding more than two numbers

Many of the pupils will have to be reminded that to add three numbers
they add the first two and then add the third to this answer.

A pupil could play this card game by himself. He should use a pack of
twenty-one cards which is made up of three of each of the numerals 0, 1,
2, 3, 4, 5 and 6. The cards are shuffled and laid out in rows of three, e.g.

6	2	1
6	0	3
5	1	4
4	2	0
6	0	3
2	3	4
1	5	5	← this row to be removed

The row of cards which gives the highest total is removed (if two rows
give an equal total then six cards are removed). The other cards are
shuffled and then laid out in threes again. The pupil could be asked to
show the teacher his last three cards or to fill in the numbers and answers
on a prepared worksheet.

27   Repeated addition patterns

Patterns produced by repeated addition of two, three, four and five can
be revised and extended. These patterns should be constructed with
materials such as towers of Unifix blocks, chains of coloured beads and
steps of Cuisenaire rods as well as being paced out on the number line
and found from hanging weights on the number balance. Remember, the
language suggested is: 'one three makes three, two threes make six, three
threes make nine, four threes make twelve' etc. As yet there is no need
for written recording nor for any attempt at memorisation of such
multiplication facts.

28   Another early multiplication pattern

Once more this is practical, oral work not as yet linked to written recording. The pupil can build up the pattern with counters, Unifix blocks, pegs, beads and Cuisenaire rods. The language here is 'four ones make four, four twos make eight, four threes make twelve, four fours make sixteen, four fives make twenty'.

29   Equal sharing

Sets of counters, blocks or beads can be shared equally between two and amongst three, four and five. The child will still share 'one to you, one to you, one to you' etc until all the material is used up. He can be encouraged to consider if two can be given at each share, even three. These are practical, oral activities not as yet linked to formal division. The activities are best structured without a remainder although the teacher may be interested to discuss with a child the sharing of thirteen between two to discover what he suggests should be done with the remainder. This could give a valuable insight into the child's understanding of number.

30   Repeated subtraction

If the pupil is given twelve blocks, he can be asked to find how many twos this can make, then how many threes, fours and sixes. The pupil can also be asked to stand at a specific position on the number line and find how many two-steps (three-steps, four-steps) will take him back to the start. No recording is associated with these practical activities except perhaps to record an answer to a word or pictorial problem.

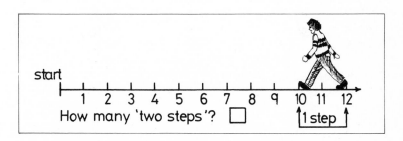

FRACTIONS

The pupil should be able to:

31   recognize, match and create quarters

32   recognize and show one half, two halves, one quarter, two quarters, three quarters and four quarters

33   record halves and quarters as $\frac{1}{2}, \frac{2}{2}, \frac{1}{4}, \frac{2}{4}, \frac{3}{4}$ and $\frac{4}{4}$.

31   Quarters

The pupil can recall what a half is, i.e. one of two equal parts. The teacher has to assess the child's understanding of equal and unequal parts, of how parts fit together to form a whole and of two equal and two unequal parts. If the pupil is having difficulty with these concepts, it may be advisable to postpone this section of work meantime.

For an understanding of a quarter as one of four equal parts, the pupil must gain experience of dividing shapes into four parts and into four equal parts. He can separate, and then combine again, shapes like these:

Equal parts match when placed on top of each other. Having focused on equal parts, the pupil can be introduced to the name one quarter. He can now be asked to find quarters, i.e. four equal parts, to match drawn lengths as in this activity.

Inside the envelope attached to the card are a variety of pieces including four quarter-pieces for each length drawn on the card. The pupil finds four equal pieces and then matches these to one of the lengths (see diagram opposite).

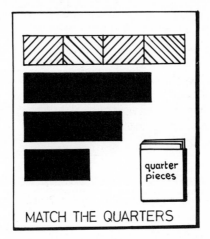

The pupil can be shown how to fold a length of string, first in two and then in two again. When cut, the child should have four quarter-pieces. An equal length of string should be kept uncut for comparison. A square of paper can be folded in different ways to produce quarters like these.

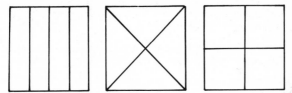

32   Halves and quarters

The pupil can be given the tan Cuisenaire rod and asked to find the rod which is one half of this. The pink rod is one half of the tan rod. Two pink rods, or two halves, match the one whole (the tan rod). This activity can then be carried out for one quarter of the tan rod. One red rod is one quarter, two red rods are two quarters, three red rods are three quarters and four red rods are four quarters which make one whole. The child can illustrate other halves and quarters, e.g.

pink	pink	pink	pink	pink	pink
red	red red	w	w w	w w w	w w w w
one	two	one	two	three	four
half	halves	quarter	quarters	quarters	quarters

An orange and red rod can be taped together to make one 'whole'.

orange		red
dark green	one half	

orange		red
light green	one quarter	

The child should be encouraged to make his own whole, halves and quarters from three strips of card (or paper)

one whole			
one half		one half	
one quarter	one quarter	one quarter	one quarter

also from three circles and from three squares of card (or paper).

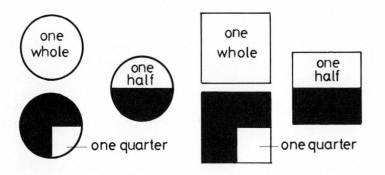

By labelling the pieces he makes, the child is introduced to the written words whole, half, quarter.

The pupil should be asked to carry out instructions using these half and quarter pieces, e.g. 'Show me one quarter of the circle. Show me two halves of the square. What have I laid out here?' If the child does not know the names circle and square, the teacher can point to the whole shape and the instruction becomes 'Show me three quarters of this shape'.

Domino game
A domino game can be played. For the slower learner the drawings can be restricted to one shape, e.g.

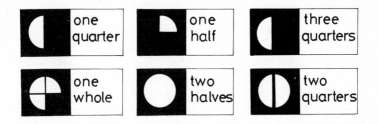

It is interesting to see if the child matches two half-circles or four quarter-circles to the words 'one whole' and/or two quarter-circles to 'one half'. These are, of course, correct matches although equivalent fractions are not mentioned at this time.

33   Notation for fractions

The symbols for halves and quarters are being introduced so that the child, if he meets them, can recognize them as another way of expressing the words one half, one quarter etc. $\frac{1}{2}$ can be seen by the pupil as 1 part out of 2 equal parts, $\frac{1}{4}$ as 1 part out of 4 equal parts, and $\frac{3}{4}$ as 3 parts out of 4 equal parts. The pupil can label diagrams which he has shaded. More cards, with the fraction symbols, can be added to the domino game, e.g.

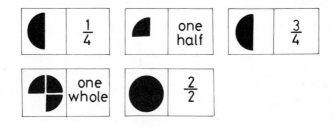

MONEY
The pupil should be able to:
34   show, recognize and record amounts 11p to 20p in one-penny coins

35   match these equivalent values
    one ten-pence coin with ten one-penny coins
    eleven to twenty pence with ten-pence and one-penny coins
    one five-pence coin with two-pence and one-penny coins
    one ten-pence coin with five two-pence coins
    one ten-pence coin with two five-pence coins
    one ten-pence coin with one five pence, two two-pence and one one-
    penny coin
36   add and take away 1p, add and take away 2p
37   relate number facts in the range of numbers one to twenty to shop-
    ping activities
38   give 'shopkeeper's change' i.e. complementary addition, in one-
    penny coins.

34   Amounts in pennies

Bags, boxes or purses should be filled with one-penny coins for amounts
11p to 20p. The pupil opens a purse, counts the coins and records the
amount on a piece of paper. The coins are returned to the coin box and
the slip of paper inserted into the empty purse. On another occasion, the
pupil opens a purse and fills it with one-penny coins for the amount
written on the slip of paper.

Purses of one-penny coins can be used to buy articles in the shop
priced at amounts in the range 11p to 20p.

35   Equivalent values

Equivalent values can be introduced to the pupil by asking him which he
would rather have for pocket money, one ten-pence coin or ten one-
penny coins. From the discussion which follows it can be established that
both these amounts are the same. The pupil can then proceed to showing
amounts from 11p to 20p in two ways, with one-penny coins and then
with ten-pence and one-penny coins. These equivalent forms of expressing an amount can be linked to shopping by filling the purses used for
shopping with either one-penny or a mixture of ten-pence and one-penny
coins to buy articles priced in the range 11p to 20p.

Later the child can be given the task of showing five pence in as many
ways as possible. The slow learner is unlikely to manage more than two
ways. This, however, gives the teacher the opportunity to show other
ways in the hope that when the child is given this activity on another
occasion he will be able to extend his contribution. The same activity can
be carried out to show ten pence in as many ways as possible. A set of
money Snap cards can be made with which an individual child can find

matching pairs of cards and later join a friend in a game of Snap. An initial set of sixteen cards can be based on amounts up to five pence and show pictures of the coins, e.g.

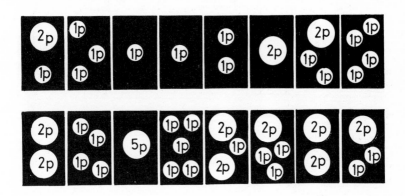

Later this set of cards can be added to with amounts expressed in numerals and in words and in time with pictures of coins and amounts up to ten pence.

36 Adding and subtracting 1p and 2p

In shopping, the pupil can be given a shopping card which asks him to buy an article for Mother, i.e. something in the price range 1p to 19p, and a sweet from the 'penny tray' for himself. The child has to add to find the total cost of his purchase. Shopping cards can also be made to give the pupil practice in adding an amount between 1p and 18p to 2p.

A subtraction activity could take place when the shop has a sale and all the prices are reduced by one pence, and on another occasion by two pence. The 'stock' of a classroom shop is usually empty jars, bottles and cartons collected by the children from their mothers. Give the pupils an interest in real prices by restricting the articles to a price range with a maximum of 20p. The containers can then be priced with 'real' prices and provide a far more worthwhile experience for the pupil. Containers can be supplemented by pretend sweets, biscuits and cakes which the children make from Plasticine, clay, Polyfilla, foam rubber etc.

37 Money calculations

Some of the children would benefit from the practice gained by applying their knowledge of number to money calculations. Perhaps a pictorial price list made up for the shop could be used, e.g.

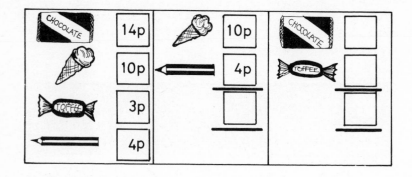

More formal calculations can be done either with the use of one-penny coins as counters or to give practice to known bonds, e.g.

9p + 8p = ☐   and   14p
                                        5p
                                        ─────

                                        ─────

If a pupil requires extra examples to reinforce his ideas of tens and units, money calculations can be related to ten-pence and one-penny coins for 'carrying' and 'decomposing', e.g.

   7p   and   13p
 +6p   − 8p
 ────   ────

 ────   ────

38   Shopkeeper's change

In the shop, the experience of the customer not giving the exact amount, but perhaps 5p, 10p, 15p and 20p made up from five-pence and ten-pence coins, can be introduced. The teacher, as shopkeeper, can show the children how to count when giving change. For example, Peter has bought a pencil costing 8p. He hands over one ten-piece coin in payment. The shopkeeper counts one-penny coins into his hand as change 'nine pence, ten pence'. Peter should check by saying 'eight pence and two pence make ten pence'. The children should give change by the counting-on method, using one-penny coins only at this time. This is, of course, a far more effective introduction to complementary addition than the abstract 'and how many more make' examples that the child meets in number work.

MEASURE
In *length,* **the pupil should be able to:**
39   order three lengths from shortest to longest, tallest to smallest etc
40   find how much longer, shorter, deeper, etc one object is in comparison with another, by using arbitrary standards.
In *volume,* **the pupil should be able to:**
41   compare two containers to find which holds more or holds less.
In *area,* **the pupil should be able to:**
42   secure the concept of conservation of area i.e. realize that matched surfaces do not change when one or both areas are shown in a different form
43   order three areas from greatest to least by placing these on top of each other or discriminating visually.
In *weight,* **the pupils should be able to:**
44   use a balance to find the heavier and the lighter of a pair of objects.
In *time,* **the pupil should be able to:**
45   recognize, state and order the days of the week
46   recognize and show on the clockface hour times, e.g. 9 o'clock, 12 o'clock.

39   Ordering lengths
Cartons or bottles can be compared at first in pairs and then as a set of three. The superlative adjectives tallest, smallest, fattest etc can be introduced through labelling flash cards, e.g.

These flash cards follow the shape of the small and tall letters to reinforce the shape of the word.
   The pupil should have activities involving flexible lengths, like ribbons, where he can find the longest and the shortest of a set.

40 Quantitative comparisons

Until now the pupil has only been involved in making qualitative comparisons, i.e. finding if an object is longer or the longest etc. He should now be given a task of seeing how much longer one object is than another. This leads the pupil into the world of arbitrary standards. The pupil has many skills to learn about measurement. In early activities the child should lay out a set of standards such as yellow rods, chalk sticks, straws etc to develop the habit of measuring along a straight line and expressing the result to the nearest whole standard. Measurements can be made along an edge and from point to point, e.g.

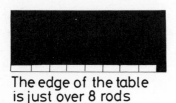

The edge of the table is just over 8 rods

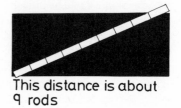

This distance is about 9 rods

In time, the pupil can be encouraged to find his own set of standards with the aim of choosing a standard which is suitable for the distance to be measured, e.g. yellow rods are ideal to measure the edge of a desk but are too small for measuring the length of the room – garden canes would be better.

When a pupil is using a set of standards to measure several distances, he should try estimating before measuring. It is important that the pupil measure at least one length with the standard before estimating. Sensible estimates of other distances can then be made by comparing the unknown distance with one already measured, e.g. 'If the edge of the desk is about 6 rods long, look at the breadth of the desk. Is this distance longer or shorter than the edge? Is it much shorter? About how many rods long do you think it is?'

41 Comparing volumes

Pairs of bottles and cartons should be compared to find which holds more or holds less. Because of the pupils' tendency to think one-dimensionally at this stage, it is important to use containers of about the same cross-section, the main difference being the height.

'Stories' can be written for the pupil to describe the relationship he finds between the containers from filling them with water or sand.

The concept of conservation of volume is difficult for many children. The pupil should be given as much experience as possible of filling, emptying and comparing containers of all shapes and sizes. These activities should be unstructured, probably a 'free choice' activity.

42   Conservation of area

The pupil should be reminded of what a surface is and be given some comparison examples. Pairs of shapes, cut out in card, can be placed one on top of the other, compared to find the larger or smaller surface and then the result recorded by a 'story arrow' like this:

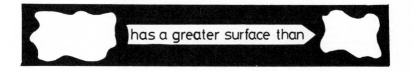

Many children will not have secured the concept of conservation of area. The teacher could carry out a Piagetian test to explore the pupil's understanding.

43   Ordering areas

The pupil can order sets of three cut-out shapes, perhaps from smallest to largest surface.

Drawings, which are easily ordered by area, can be shown to the child with the instruction to colour the shape with the smallest surface blue, the largest surface red etc.

44   Using a balance

The pupil has already been introduced to the balance. Using this he can be reminded of how to identify which object is heavy and which is light. He should also be able to recognize how the balance shows two objects to be about the same weight.

In this section of the work the child is introduced to the vocabulary of 'heavier' and 'lighter'. At first the child can find which of two parcels or objects is the heavier or lighter. Then he can carry out a sorting exercise by being given about five objects and being asked to find which are heavier than, for example, the blue box. The blue box is placed on one pan of the balance and each object in turn is placed in the other pan. The results might be recorded by placing the objects on a sheet of paper.

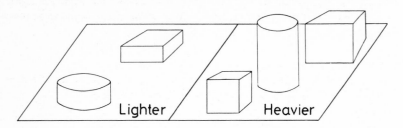

For most of the objects, size can be related to weight, i.e. large objects are heavier, but one or two small heavy articles might be used and the results discussed with the child.

45 Days of the week
Time sequences have been introduced to the child as ordered events, e.g. drinking milk is carried out by a series of actions:

1 Collect the container and a straw.
2 Make a hole in the container.
3 Insert the straw.
4 Lift the container and straw.
5 Drink.

He has also met expressions like yesterday, today, tomorrow and possibly morning, afternoon, evening and/or night. These sequences can be revised and more examples created. The days of the week may be written on the classroom blackboard. Events can be linked to the day on which they occur. The pupil should recognize the names of the days from flash cards—ideally cards which he has helped to make. These cards can be ordered from Sunday to Saturday. The pupil should be able to state which day comes after, and which day comes before, Monday, Tuesday etc to Friday. Asking which day comes before Sunday should encourage the child to see this sequence in a circular pattern. The pupil can also show sequences of cards beginning with any day, e.g. Wednesday,

Thursday etc. The pupil can find out that there are seven different names of days and seven days make up one week. The understanding of any seven days in sequence making up a week may be difficult for the slow learners so this point does not need to be emphasized just now.

A calendar can be discussed so that the child can recognize the names of the days in this context. The *Radio Times* and *TV Times* can be looked at to see how the days are written into the page headings and the order of the days considered. A collection of cuttings from newspapers, magazines and other printed matter, where the names of days occur, can be made by a group of children.

46 The clock face

The children are already familiar with the number line when it is expressed horizontally and/or vertically. For this section of work it is a great help if they have made a circular number line.

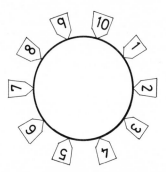

This makes it easier to introduce a circular number line from 1 to 12. The clock face can then be seen as another example of a number line. The large hand of the clock should be fixed pointing to 12 while the small hand can be made to move around the face pointing to the numbers from 1 to 12. Once the pupil is familiar with this movement of the small hand, he can be asked to make it point to specific numbers. It can be explained that we use the clock to help us to know and to tell others when events happen. John begins school when the small hand is at nine. This is called nine o'clock (nine on the clock would be a good explanation for the pupil and make more sense to him than the archaic 'nine of the clock'). The child can now link daily occurrences to hourly times, e.g. lunchtime is twelve o'clock, Daddy comes home at six o'clock. Some children may realize the small hand goes around the face twice every day, but this does not need to be highlighted at this time.

SHAPE
The pupil should be able to:
47 recognize the edges (straight or curved) of a three-dimensional shape
48 recognize the corners of a three-dimensional shape
49 create three-dimensional shapes in clay (or Plasticine)
50 establish relationships among three-dimensional shapes such as 'has as many faces as' 'has as many edges as' and 'is the same shape as'
51 sort three-dimensional shapes into 'families' of cubes, cylinders, cuboids, cones and spheres.

47 Edges of three-dimensional shapes
The pupil has already been introduced to faces. He can be reminded of these by being asked to point out and count the faces of a variety of shapes.

Since two faces meet at an edge, the pupil can be asked to feel the edges of shapes. The edges can be straight or curved. The rolling activities, carried out when curved faces were investigated, can be considered again so that the child sees the cone rolling on its curved edge, the cream tub and the cylinder rolling on both their curved edges.

Since the number of edges changes from shape to shape, the pupils can find out how many different edges the shapes from their collection have, e.g. the sphere has no edges, the cone has one, the cylinder two, the wedge of apple three, the box twelve etc.

48 Corners of three-dimensional shapes
Edges meet at corners. The pupil can feel and count the number of corners which the shapes have. Some shapes have no corners (e.g. cylinder, sphere), others have many (e.g. the box has eight, the square-based pyramid has five).

Cartons can be sorted by the number of corners, e.g. shapes which have eight corners, shapes which have more than five corners, shapes which have less than seven corners. The shapes are placed in boundaries. The pupil need not get involved in the names of the shapes or any written recording at this time.

49 Making shapes
Making three-dimensional shapes in clay focuses the pupil's attention on whether faces are curved or flat and how many there are; whether edges are straight or curved and how many edges and corners there are. Curved faces and edges are formed by rolling, whereas flattening and

pressing with a ruler will help to make faces flat and edges straight.

The slow learners will probably benefit by being given a specific task such as 'make a shape like this one' and having a model to copy. In time, they might like to construct a shape of their own choice. This can be discussed with a friend so that the pupil has practice in talking about edges, faces and corners.

50   Shape relationships

Using a collection of wooden shapes or cartons, the pupil can be asked to find shapes which have the same edge, face and corner properties. From the activities of counting the number of faces, edges and corners, the pupil will have found that some shapes have the same number of edges, faces and corners, but that they differ in size. Sets of shapes can be formed to show shapes which have the same number of faces. Similar-shaped containers can also be sorted.

51   'Families' of three-dimensional shapes

Until now the properties of the shapes have been considered rather than their names. Now that the pupil is aware that there are sets of shapes which are alike in the number of corners, edges and faces, he can be introduced to 'families' and the name given to each shape in that family. There are arguments about what names the pupil should use—box or cuboid, ball or sphere? The teacher should note the name used by the pupil and ask herself the following questions: Does it discriminate between shapes clearly? Can he communicate to others using this name? If the name used fits these criteria by all means allow the pupil to continue to use it. The teacher is advised to use the mathematical name, perhaps with the exception of 'ball', and so provide a model for the child to adopt, when he is ready to do so.

The names and shapes of the cube and cone families will be easy for the pupils. Cylinder and cuboid may be more difficult names although the shapes are easily identified. Collections of these families can be made. Sorting activities can be carried out and the names, written on flash cards, can be used to label the sets.

Shapes in the environment can be identified as members of the families, e.g. the chimney as a cylinder, the modern office block as a cuboid, the church spire as a cone. Models can be made like those shown on page 110.

The pupil can also be introduced to pictures of three-dimensional shapes so that he relates these to the cartons and wooden shapes he has been using for this work.

PICTORIAL REPRESENTATION
The pupil should be able to:
52   construct and interpret simple data as a pictograph.

52   Pictographs
In Stage 1, the pupil represented data with three-dimensional objects such as biscuits and toy cars. In Stage 2, pictures of objects are used to represent the information which has to be recorded. The pupils enjoy representing facts about themselves so it is suggested that each child draws a picture of himself on a rectangular piece of paper. These uniform sheets of paper can be used to make displays of data, e.g. colour of eyes. In this example, the children have matched the drawing of their head to samples of light and dark hair.

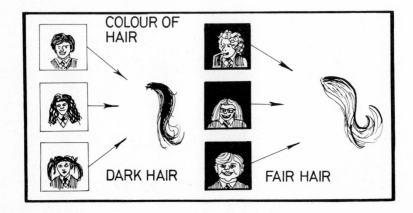

This block graph has been formed by the children's drawings of themselves. The drawings are arranged close to each other in columns built up from a 'start line'.

It is important that once the display has been made, a discussion takes place which involves the children in interpretation of the representation, e.g. Are there more blue-eyed pupils than brown-eyed? Are there a greater number of pupils in this group who have dark hair rather than fair hair? How many more girls are there in this group than boys?

Measurement activities can be illustrated either by individual children or by a group, e.g.

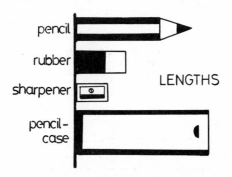

Here the child represents the length of objects by this drawing of them. In discussion he can comment on which objects are shorter than the pencil, longer than the rubber etc.

Reference

A series of mathematics workbooks which might be used to help the pupil achieve the objectives listed in Stage 2 is Aileen Duncan's *Numbers and Words* (Books 5-8), published by Ward Lock Educational.

STAGE 3

Number
There are three parts in the number work of Stage 3.

1   Numbers 21 to 30
This part contains the recognition of sets of these cardinalities, matching these sets to the appropriate numerals and reproducing these numerals. A counting pattern is established. Addition and subtraction of tens and units are detailed in steps of increasing difficulty.

2   Numbers 31 to 99
This part begins with the introduction of new numerals. These are then related to the appropriate number of tens and units. Repeated addition activities develop patterns of twos, threes, fours etc. The pupil then meets the two and three times tables. There is also division by sharing and grouping materials.

3   Numbers 0 to 100
In this part the pupil tackles number sequences and patterns. Multiplication facts from the two, three, four, five and ten times tables are met and then linked to division work. A section is included on word problems.

Fractions
The learner is introduced to thirds and fifths as well as mixed fractions and a family of equivalent fractions.

Money
The 50p coin is used in money activities and calculations.

Measure
In area, volume and weight activities, the pupil uses a variety of arbitrary standards, whereas in length the need for universal standards is established and the pupil measures in metres and in centimetres.

Time is now recognized and recorded on the clock in terms of half past, quarter past and quarter to the hour. The months of the year are also introduced.

Shape
After further work on three-dimensional shapes, the pupil meets two-

dimensional shapes as the faces of cartons and boxes. Edges and corners of these shapes are recognized and counted. Rectangles, circles, triangles and squares are identified by the number and type of edges. Symmetric and tiling activities complete this section on shape.

Pictorial representation
Block graphs, arrow diagrams and tables are constructed and discussed.

NUMBERS 21 TO 30
The pupil should be able to:
1 recognize, name and create sets of cardinalities twenty-one to thirty
    recognize, name and match to the appropriate set, the numerals 21 to 30
    reproduce the numerals 21 to 30
    order sets, number names and numerals within the range twenty-one to thirty
2 show an understanding of place value for tens and units and be able to discriminate between numbers such as 21 and 12
3 add
    tens and units to units, where the sum of units is less than ten
    tens and units to tens and units, where the sum of both the tens and the units is less than ten
    tens and units to units, where the exchange of ten units for one ten occurs
    tens and units to tens and units, involving the exchange of ten units for one ten
4 subtract
    units from tens and units, with no decomposition of ten
    tens and units from tens and units, with no decomposition of ten
    units from tens and units, with the decomposition of one ten to ten units
    tens and units from tens and units, with the decomposition of one ten to ten units

1 Numbers 21 to 30
The numbers one to twenty, which the pupil has already met, have introduced him to the structure of our number system. In Stage 2, the pupil used the number pieces to show ten units as one ten, eleven units as one ten and one unit etc. The use of the number names eleven, twelve and thirteen rather than names such as 'teny-one', 'teny-two' and 'teny-three'

etc means that the pupil has not as yet met the number-name pattern which is used for the numbers greater than twenty, i.e. a new word for the number of tens followed by the known pattern of 'one, two, three' etc.

This pattern of number names for counting is now introduced. It is important to emphasize that counting is not seen as a chanting exercise but as a grouping activity. By handling the objects as each is counted it is possible to reinforce the concept of the number name referring to the cardinality of the counted set, i.e. when the pupil says 'twenty-two', 'twenty-three' etc he is stating how many objects he has counted at that moment.

The skill of counting from one to twenty should be revised by asking the pupil to find how many are in sets of pencils, books, buttons etc. During these activities the teacher can begin to encourage the child to lay out the objects in groups of ten as he counts.

It is now appropriate to extend the pupil's range of number names by the teacher counting and grouping members of sets with a cardinality less than, or equal to, thirty. The pupil can practise these new names as he counts and groups cubes, beads and rods.

From these naming and grouping activities it will be easy for the pupil to match numerals to sets, e.g. twenty-four is counted as two tens and four so this is written as 24.

Some measuring activities may require the pupil to count rods, straws or pieces of chalk. As well as giving counting practice this is an opportunity for the pupil to record his answer. Practice in writing the numerals will also be necessary.

Rather than extend the number line, as in Stages 1 and 2, this is a good time for the pupils to produce a new wall number-line as shown in the diagram:

The numerals can be written on cards and then placed in position.

Game

Here is a game which will give the pupils practice in ordering number names and numerals in sequences. Four to six players can play. A set of numeral cards for 1 to 30 are shuffled and dealt to the players, including an extra 'hand'. The top card of this extra hand is turned face up. The players use this card as the first of a sequence and place consecutive numeral cards from their hands face up in front of them, stating the number name as each card is played. When the sequence cannot be continued due to unavailability of cards (some are unusable in the extra hand), the player of the last card plays any card of his choice to begin a new sequence. The first player to play all his cards is the winner.

2 Place value—numbers as tens and units

An exchange game to remind pupils that ten units match one ten rod in the number pieces is useful at the beginning of this section of work.

Game

A standard dice marked from one to six is used. Each player in turn throws the dice and takes the appropriate number of units from a box of pieces. Whenever possible ten units are exchanged for one ten. The first player to have three tens is the winner. Cards as shown in the diagram can be used by each player. Units are stored in the marked strip and when this is full the ten units are exchanged for one ten which is placed in the rectangle which has space for three tens.

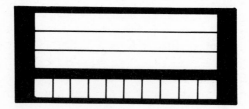

The pupils in Stage 2 used Mister cards (page 77) to show the numbers ten to nineteen as one ten and some units. House cards can be used to show the numbers twenty to twenty-nine as two tens and some units, e.g.

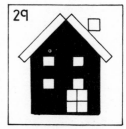

The two tens form the edges of the roof and the units can be placed on squares as windows, a chimney and a door.

The pupil can now represent numbers with the number pieces on the notation card. Number pieces can also be placed on the notation card either by the teacher or by a class mate, for the pupil to identify the number represented. Worksheet examples using diagrams can give the pupil further practice.

When the pupil can use the ten and unit pieces with ease, he can be asked to show two numbers which involve a reversal of digits, e.g. 21 and 12. The correct representation of these numbers could lead to a discussion in which the pupil might reveal his understanding of place value.

If possible, equip each child with a box of wooden pieces. Nine tens and eighteen units are adequate for the representation of numbers and for calculations at this stage. Two sets of number cards, preferably of two colours (one for tens and one for units) and ranging from 0 to 9 would also be useful, as well as a notation card.

Domino game
A domino game based on different ways of expressing numbers can be played. Make up the domino cards based on four different forms of expression for seven numbers, e.g. 21, 12, 23, 13, 30, 26, 16.

thirty	26		2 tens and 6 units	13		thirteen	three tens

30	two tens and three units		twenty-three	one ten and three units		1 ten and 3 units	21

3   Addition

The pupil can begin by using the number pieces and recording only the answer. Then he can record the whole calculation linking the numerals to the pieces as he lays them out and then collects them together. Finally, the pupil can work the addition without using the pieces. It is wise not to rush this last stage or the pupil will resort to counting on his fingers.

Step 1   Tens and units, where the sum of the units is less than or equal to nine
Some examples can be 23 + 5, 24 + 3, 20 + 6. Every opportunity should

be made for the pupil to realize that these 'new' calculations are related to the addition bonds he already knows, i.e. 23 + 5 should be seen as 20 + (3 + 5). This use of the associative law is well illustrated when working with the pieces:

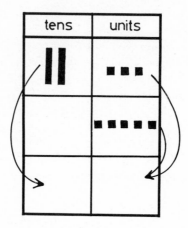

Step 2 *Tens and units to tens and units, where the sum of neither the tens nor the units is greater than nine*

Some examples can be 13 + 14, 16 + 12, 10 + 9. The language developed when using the pieces is shown in the example of 15 + 13. 'Fifteen is one ten and five units. Thirteen is one ten and three units. Five units and three units are eight units. One ten and one ten are two tens. Two tens and eight units are twenty-eight'.

Step 3 *Tens and units to units, where the exchange of ten units for one ten occurs*

Some examples can be 18 + 7, 14 + 9, 26 + 4. After collecting the unit pieces together, the pupil will find he can exchange ten units for one ten. This ten is put with the other tens.

Step 4 *Tens and units, involving the exchange of ten units for one ten*

Only additions which sum to thirty are possible in this range of numbers e.g. 15 + 15, 12 + 18, 11 + 19.

An example (14 + 16) in this section could be worked using the pieces in the following way. 'Fourteen is one ten and four units. Sixteen is one ten and six units. Four units and six units are ten units. Ten units is one ten and no units. One ten, one ten and one ten (or one ten and two tens) are three tens. Three tens and no units are thirty'.

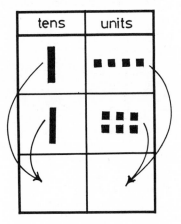

It is a matter of opinion as to how best to add the exchanged ten. It can be added separately or through a combination with the lower number of tens. Each of these methods would lead to appropriate recordings.

$$\begin{array}{ccc}
14 & 14 & 14 \\
+1{,}6 & +16 \text{ or } & +_2\!\!/\!\!16 \\
\hline
0 & 0 & 0 \\
& {}_1 &
\end{array}$$

Game

Here is a game to consolidate some of the addition work in this range of numbers. Each player contributes a set of numeral cards 0 to 9. These are formed into a pack which is shuffled. Each player is dealt one card and the remainder of the pack is placed face down in the centre of the table. Each player in turn may take one card from the top of the pack. A player adds each card he receives to those he already had. He wishes to achieve a total of twenty-five or less. If he decides to take a card from the pack and this makes his total more than twenty-five, he takes no further part in that round of the game. When each player has decided that he does not want any more cards, he shows his cards and states the total sum of the numbers. The player with a total of twenty-five, or if no player has this sum, the player with a sum less than but nearest to twenty-five, scores a point. The first player to gain five points is the winner. One child should keep a note of the points won by each player.

4 Subtraction

So far the subtraction sign has been interpreted as 'take away'. This expression is still used in this section of the work.

Step 1   Units from tens and units, with no decomposition of ten
Some examples can be $29 - 6$, $28 - 3$, $25 - 4$. The pupil should follow the method suggested in Stage 2 for carrying out the subtraction using the number pieces. The larger number is represented by pieces on the notation card. Pieces to represent the smaller number are laid at the right-hand side of the card. The answer is shown by the pieces left on the notation card, e.g. $27 - 5 = 22$. Pupils should realize that pieces can be combined again to form the original number.

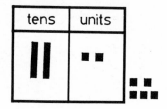

Step 2   Tens and units from tens and units, with no decomposition of ten
Some examples can be $28 - 11$, $25 - 13$, $23 - 20$, $26 - 23$.

Step 3   Units from tens and units, with the decomposition of one ten to ten units
Some examples could be $24 - 8$, $27 - 9$ $21 - 6$. Examples in this section can be worked with the materials like this. $22 - 5$ 'Twenty-two is two tens and two units. I want to take away five units but I can't.

tens	units
❚❚	■ ■

'I exchange one ten for ten units. (The ten units are taken from the box of pieces and the one ten placed there in exchange.)

tens	units
I	■ ■ ■ ■ ■ ■ ■ ■ ■ ■ ■ ■

'Five units from twelve units leaves seven units. One ten and seven units is seventeen. Twenty-two take away five leaves seventeen'.

tens	units
I	■ ■ ■ ■ ■ ■ ■

■ ■ ■ ■ ■

Step 4   Tens and units from tens and units, with the decomposition of one ten to ten units
Some examples can be $23 - 15$, $24 - 18$, $30 - 21$. Recording which mirrors the use of the pieces would be like this:

$$\begin{array}{r} 25 \\ -17 \\ \hline \end{array} \longrightarrow \begin{array}{r} ^1\!\!\not{2}\,5 \\ -1\;7 \\ \hline \end{array} \longrightarrow \begin{array}{r} ^1\!\!\not{2}\,5 \\ -1\;7 \\ \hline 8 \end{array}$$

NUMBERS 31 TO 99
The pupil should be able to:
  5   **recognize, name, identify as tens and units, and match to the appropriate set, the numerals 31 to 99**
      reproduce the numerals 31 to 99
      order sets, number names and numerals within the range thirty-one to ninety-nine
  6   **recognize and use the ordinal names twenty-first to ninety-ninth**

7　recognize and state odd and even numbers
8　add without, and with, the exchange of ten units for one ten with numbers whose sum is less than or equal
　　to fifty
　　to ninety-nine
9　subtract without, and with, the decomposition of one ten to ten units with numbers within the range
　　zero to fifty
　　zero to ninety-nine
10　construct patterns of repeated addition
11　construct the two and the three times tables
12　carry out equal sharing activities without, or with, a remainder, between two and amongst three for sets with a cardinality less than or equal to thirty
13　carry out repeated subtraction activities, without, or with, a remainder, for twos and threes in sets of cardinalities zero to thirty
14　carry out complementary addition in the range of sums zero to twenty
15　find the difference between numbers in the range zero to twenty.

5　Numbers 31 to 99

The pupil should now be able to see these numbers as an extension of facts he already knows, i.e. the number names have the pattern of a word for the tens followed by one, two, three etc to nine, and that the name and numeral are best linked to sets of objects grouped in tens and units. The pupils can carry out counting exercises with sticks, beads, counters etc.

In the example shown in the diagram the pupil has counted forty-three sticks. Such an arrangement in tens makes it easy for a class mate to check a pupil's answer or for the pupil to carry out a recount as well reinforcing the place-value aspect of each number.

Pupils can also make traffic or pupil counts at this stage. Peter recorded a tally of traffic which passed him like this:

> Cars   卌 卌 卌 卌 卌 卌 卌 || 37

and Jean made a note of the pupils passing through the school entrance with the same 'five-bar gates'. Such tallies are easy to construct, to identify and to check.

To give practice in ordering, a pupil can be given a pack of ten numeral cards and asked to place these in sequence from smallest to greatest or greatest to smallest. (Use any ten consecutive numbers.)

Number pieces can be laid out on the notation card to represent numbers and the results recorded on a prepared worksheet, e.g.

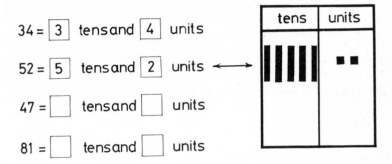

$34 = \boxed{3}$ tens and $\boxed{4}$ units

$52 = \boxed{5}$ tens and $\boxed{2}$ units   ⟷

$47 = \boxed{}$ tens and $\boxed{}$ units

$81 = \boxed{}$ tens and $\boxed{}$ units

Game

Here is a game two children can play combining their sets of numeral cards. The cards are made into a pack of twenty. The pack contains two sets of the numerals 0 to 9. The pack is shuffled and placed face down in the centre of the table. Each child is dealt two cards from the pack by another pupil, the teacher or one of the players. The child looks at both his cards and, by positioning, makes the largest number he can, e.g. if he is dealt a 5 and an 8, the largest number he can make is 85. The player who makes the larger number claims the four cards. When all the cards have been dealt and claimed, the player with more cards is the winner. If this game is played by more than two players, more numeral cards should be used.

6   Ordinal names twenty-first to ninety-ninth

The pupil should not only learn the ordinal number names but also realize that these expressions refer to the position or order of one member in the set, e.g. 'Turn over the thirty-ninth card in the pack'.

7 Odd and even numbers

The pupil can be told that an even number is one where the members can be arranged in twos (pairs). Eight and twenty are even numbers. Five and seventeen cannot be laid out in pairs, so these numbers are not even, they are odd. In time the pupil will realize that even numbers and multiples of two are the same set of numbers.

8 Addition

As in the last section, the examples should be graded. The numbers should be tackled in two cycles: first, numbers to fifty and then repeating the graded examples for numbers to ninety-nine.

1   Addition of tens and units to units where sum of units is less than 10, e.g. 32 + 4, 33 + 6, 41 + 7, 45 + 2; 81 + 4, 72 + 3, 94 + 4, 65 + 4.
2   Addition of tens and units to tens and units, where the sum of both the tens and units is less than 10, e.g. 23 + 13, 24 + 21, 32 + 17, 36 + 11; 41 + 18, 35 + 42, 43 + 41, 55 + 40.
3   Addition of tens and units to units, involving the exchange of ten units to one ten, e.g. 28 + 5, 32 + 9, 37 + 7, 42 + 8; 48 + 6, 51 + 9, 63 + 8, 75 + 7, 89 + 9.
4   Addition of tens and units to tens and units, involving the exchange of ten units to one ten, e.g. 19 + 18, 23 + 18, 24 + 26; 25 + 27, 31 + 29, 36 + 36, 47 + 49.

Examples should be worked using the number pieces to establish understanding of the operation and to give confidence in the use of the basic number bonds. 38 + 46 'Thirty-eight is three tens and eight units.

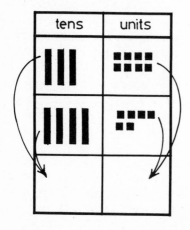

ten units are exchanged for one ten

Forty-six is four tens and six units. Eight units and six units are fourteen units. Fourteen units is one ten and four units. Three tens, four tens and one ten (or three tens and five tens) are eight tens. Eight tens and four tens are eighty-four'.

9 Subtraction

Examples are graded within two suggested ranges of numbers: to fifty and to ninety-nine. It is suggested that a pupil tackles the range to fifty type of examples first with the number pieces and then as abstract calculations. This cycle of work is then repeated for the range to ninety-nine examples.

1 Subtraction of units from tens and units, with no decomposition of ten, e.g. $34 - 2$, $37 - 4$, $46 - 6$, $48 - 6$; $55 - 2$, $69 - 3$, $77 - 1$, $82 - 2$, $91 - 0$.

2 Subtraction of tens and units from tens and units, with no decomposition of ten, e.g. $37 - 15$, $35 - 22$, $49 - 17$, $47 - 22$, $44 - 30$; $53 - 12$, $64 - 21$, $78 - 35$, $86 - 45$, $95 - 50$, $98 - 76$.

3 Subtraction of units from tens and units, with the decomposition of one ten to ten units, e.g. $32 - 4$, $33 - 8$, $45 - 7$, $48 - 9$; $51 - 8$, $65 - 8$, $73 - 7$, $81 - 4$.

4 Subtraction of tens and units from tens and units, with the decomposition of one ten to ten units, e.g. $35 - 19$, $37 - 28$, $41 - 12$, $44 - 26$, $42 - 37$; $56 - 18$, $68 - 29$, $70 - 37$, $85 - 59$, $93 - 76$.

When writing out worksheets or workcards of examples, refer to Stage 1 sections 25, 32 and 34, to Stage 2 sections 10, 12, 19, 21 and 23 so that most of the basic number bonds can be included. This seems to be a good time to extend the pupil's mathematical language. He can be introduced to terms like 'subtract' and 'minus', and use these as well as 'take away'.

10 Repeated addition patterns

Materials suggested for use in this section are the number line, Cuisenaire rods and the number balance.

The number line

A number line for 0 to 99 made by pupils can run horizontally along the classroom wall. Strips of card lengths of 2, 3, 4 etc to 9 intervals, equal to those on the number line, are made separately. A pupil is given one of these strips and asked to record the 'stations' as he moves the strip along the line.

Cuisenaire rods
On this occasion the child lays out the rods for the chosen pattern in columns or rows. All the rods will be of the same colour, e.g. if a pattern of threes is produced, all the rods used will be light green. The pupil should record the total of each column, preferably by adding mentally. Because the rods are unmarked the pupil cannot count in ones.

Number balance
This piece of equipment is best used when the pupil can calculate the answer and wants to check that he is correct.

Weights are placed on one number on the left-hand side of the balance, e.g. one on three, two on three, three on three, four on three etc, and each time the answer is recorded on the right-hand side of the balance by weights placed on the appropriate numbers, e.g. on three, on six, on nine, on ten and on two, on ten and on five etc, to achieve a balance.

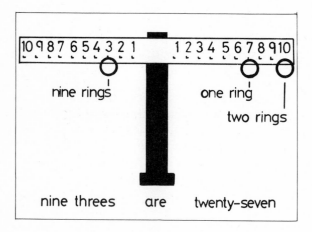

11 The two and three times tables
The pupil can use counters, Unifix blocks and beads to create the patterns for these tables. The use of colour should help to show the pattern clearly, e.g. if the two times table is being created, two colours should be used and if the three times table is being formed, three colours should be used.

Two forms of language are suitable here: 'two ones, two twos, two threes' etc, or 'two times one, two times two, two times three' etc. The first form might be used with the concrete materials and the second related to recording these patterns.

Once the pupil has constructed each table in a variety of materials, he can be given several recording exercises to practise the multiplication facts he is learning. The teacher should at first keep to formats which record the 'table' in sequence, e.g.

$1 + 1 = 2$	2 times 1 is $\boxed{2}$	$2 \times 1 = \boxed{2}$
$2 + 2 = 4$	2 times 2 is $\square$	$2 \times 2 = \boxed{4}$
$3 + 3 = 6$	2 times 3 is $\square$	$2 \times 3 = \square$
$4 + 4 = 8$	2 times 4 is $\square$	$2 \times 4 = \square$

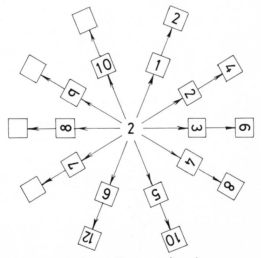

A two times wheel

1	2	3	4	5	6	7	8	9	10
$\times 2$	$\times 2$	$\times 2$	$\times 2$	$\times 2$	$\times 2$	$\times 2$	$\times 2$	$\times 2$	$\times 2$
2	4	6	8	10	12	14	16	—	—

Later formats (which can be used to record the multiplication facts in random order) are:

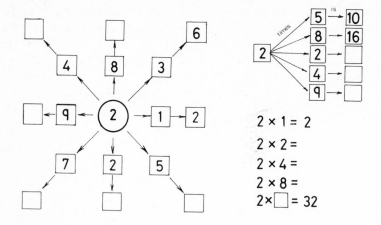

$$2 \times 1 = 2$$
$$2 \times 2 =$$
$$2 \times 4 =$$
$$2 \times 8 =$$
$$2 \times \square = 32$$

The number balance can be used to allow the child to check the facts he is beginning to know. For the two and three times tables, the pupil hangs two, then three weights on each number on the left-hand side of the balance in turn and records the answer each time with weights on the right-hand side.

A Bingo game can consolidate these multiplication facts.

Two-times Bingo

Use a spinner marked 1 to 10. Each player has a card which shows six numbers. The numbers are multiples of 2, from 2 to 20 inclusive. No two cards should show the same six multiples.

Each pupil in turn uses the spinner, multiplies the number shown by two and calls out the answer. All pupils who have this product on their cards cover it with a counter. If ten is called and a pupil has 10 marked twice on his card, he is allowed to cover only one of them on this occasion. The first player with a card where all six numbers are covered with counters is the winner. A set of cards can be made showing multiples of 3 for a 'Three-times' Bingo game.

12 Equal sharing activities

Bags of counters or blocks can be given to the pupil to be shared between two plates. The result is recorded as 'Each share is $\square$'. At first all the sets to be shared should contain an even number of members. Later the pupil can be faced with the problem of sharing a set with an odd number of members. Answers here can be recorded as 'Each share is ☐ and there is ☐ left'. These activities should also be carried out sharing amongst three. Again sharing should at first be without a remainder and later with a remainder.

13 Repeated subtraction activities

Counters or blocks can be grouped into a sorting apparatus such as margarine tubs. The pupil is asked to find 'how many twos are in this set?' Where there is a remainder, the activity is carried out and recorded like this:

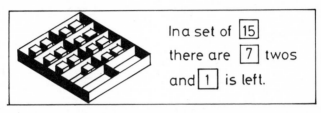

In a set of ⏐15⏐ there are ⏐7⏐ twos and ⏐1⏐ is left.

The number line can be used with the two- and three-strip (see section 10). If the pupil is asked to find 'how many threes are in fifteen?' he lines up the right-hand edge of the three strip with fifteen and then by moving backwards, i.e. to the left, counts how many times he can fit in the strip.

Worksheet examples where number lines have been drawn for the pupil to mark jumps are excellent practice, e.g.

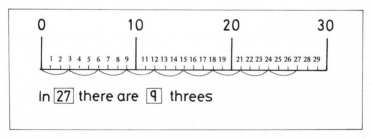

In ⏐27⏐ there are ⏐9⏐ threes

These worksheet examples are also suitable for questions with remainders.

14 Complementary addition

This aspect of work was tackled as 'twin sums' in Stage 2 section 24. This type of example should be worked again by the pupil, e.g.

$12 + 3 = ☐$ $9 + 8 = ☐$
$12 + ☐ = 15$ $9 + ☐ = 17$

The number balance can be used. A weight is placed on the 8 on the left-hand side and a weight on the 10 and the 4 on the right-hand side of the balance. The pupil finds on which number on the left-hand side he has to place the weight to achieve a balance—in this case on 6 (i.e. 8 and 6 are 14).

Here are two games which will help the pupil to perform complementary addition calculations.

Seven

Each player is given fifteen counters, the remainder being placed in a central box. The aim is to be left with seven counters. Each player in turn throws the dice (marked one to six) and must decide whether to take counters for the number indicated from the box or to place counters in the box. Through taking and putting back, each player tries to be left with seven blocks. The first to achieve this number is the winner.

Tens

Two sets of numeral cards for 0 to 10 are shuffled and laid out in an array of rows and columns face down on the table. Each player in sequence turns over a card, calculates what other card is required to give a total of ten and then tries to turn over the card with that number. If the pair of cards give a total of ten they are kept by the player; if not, the cards are placed face down again in the same positions in the array. The player who collects most cards is the winner.

15   Difference between

Some revision of 'as many as', 'more' and 'less' between sets of objects is necessary at the beginning of this section of work. To find the difference between two sets, the pupil should lay out each set and where possible match members. The subset of unmatched members shows the difference between the sets, e.g.

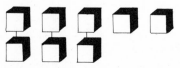

The difference between five and three is two

The pupil should work examples and record the answers preferably on a prepared worksheet, e.g.

The *difference* between   4 and 1 is ☐
The difference between   9 and 2 is ☐
The difference between 13 and 8 is ☐

NUMBERS 0 TO 100
The pupil should be able to:

16   recognize, name, identify as one hundred and as ten tens, and match to the appropriate set, the numeral 100
reproduce the numeral 100

17   order sets, names and numerals within the range zero to one hundred
state the highest, the lowest, the greatest and the smallest number in a given set

18   recognize and use the ordinal names first to hundredth

19   construct and recognize number patterns based on addition and subtraction, e.g. {10, 20, 30 . . .}, {1, 3, 5, 7 . . .}, {4, 8, 12, 16 . . .}

20   add and subtract any two numbers where these numbers and the answer lie within the range zero to one hundred

21   calculate the total of several numbers where addition and subtraction is included

22   construct the four, five and ten times tables

23   recognize and use the multiplication facts from the two, three, four, five and ten times tables

24   carry out sharing activities between two and amongst three, four, five and ten
carry out repeated subtraction of twos, threes, fours, fives and tens for the range of numbers in the appropriate 'tables'

25   interpret and carry out calculations to answer simple written-word problems involving addition and subtraction.

16   One hundred

The pupil should recall that ten unit-pieces match one ten-piece in the materials used to represent our number system, and can be introduced to the 'flat' as ten ten-pieces or as one hundred. The pupil should now lay out ten rows of ten unit-pieces to see that these also match one hundred and through counting these units, replacing each ten units with one ten-piece as he does so, the pupil can find the number name 'one hundred' follows 'ninety-nine'. Finally the pupil should exchange the ten ten-pieces for the one hundred-piece.

A discussion as to where the hundred piece should be placed on the notation card will result in the pupil making a new notation card with three columns as shown in this diagram:

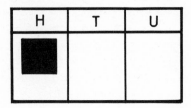

The hundred piece presented like this should be linked to the numeral 100, i.e. one hundred, no tens and no units.

The numeral 100 should now be added to the classroom number line. The pupil can be asked to carry out counting activities in which the objects are laid out in groups of ten as the counting proceeds. Some of the sets to be counted should have a cardinality of one hundred.

17 Ordering and sequences
The pupils can make this game for themselves. Each player in the group writes five two-digit numbers, each on a square of paper. All the squares of paper are collected, shuffled and placed in a pile, face down, in the centre of the table. A player turns over the top unseen square and says that number and the next four numbers in the counting sequence. If a player is in difficulty he can consult the classroom number line.

18 Ordinal number names
Press cuttings listing the finishing order of competitors in events could be useful discussion material, e.g. 'Which football team came twelfth in the First Division?' 'In which place did John Brown finish in the cross-country run?'

Alphabetical lists can be compiled about pupils in the school, and the pupil could then identify the forty-second pupil etc.

19 Number patterns
Number patterns can be recorded on a 'hundred square' (i.e. numbers written out in rows of ten on a square card) using counters, e.g. the counters could be placed by repeatedly adding on 3 (i.e. on 6, 9, 12 etc). Subtraction patterns can also be created on the hundred square and the

positions of the counters recorded, e.g. 100, 95, 90, 85, 80, 75 etc and 100, 98, 96, 94, 92 etc.

20   Addition and subtraction

As well as working given examples, the pupil can have fun constructing and then calculating answers for his own addition examples. These can be created by the pupil in the following way. He selects any four cards from a pack containing numerals 0 to 5, and he then constructs as many sums as possible with the four numerals, records the calculations and finds the answer, e.g. the four cards showing 3, 5, 2, 1 would produce the calculations

35	53	32	23	52	25
+21	+12	+51	+15	+31	+13
—	—	—	—	—	—

together with their commutative equivalents. The pupil may include examples of commutative equivalents, e.g.

21	and	35
+35		+21
—		—

If he does so, this provides an opportunity to discuss the commutative property of addition.

To allow the pupil to construct subtraction examples let him select any four cards from the numerals 0 to 9 and each two-digit number which can be formed should be taken away from a given number such as 99, e.g. four cards (2, 8, 6, 1) would produce these calculations.

99	99	99	99	99	99	99	99	99	99	99	99
−28	−82	−26	−62	−86	−68	−61	−16	−81	−18	−21	−12
—	—	—	—	—	—	—	—	—	—	—	—

21   Mixed addition and subtraction

$14 + 27 - 19$, $45 - 21 + 16$, $92 - 16 - 14$. In examples of this type the pupil has to understand that the operation sign states what has to happen to the number which follows it, e.g. fourteen, add twenty-seven, subtract nineteen.

For some examples if materials are used, they have to be handled with some thought. $45 - 21 + 16$ The pupil sets out forty-five as four tens and five units and then performs the subtraction by physically removing the one unit and two tens which represent twenty-one. This leaves two tens and four units. It is only now that the child considers the third number, sixteen, and places one ten and six units on the board. He adds his unit pieces; four and six are ten. Ten units are exchanged for one ten. Two tens and one ten are three tens. Three tens and one ten are four tens. Four tens and no units are forty.

Some of the children might be able to check if a given square of numbers is a magic square i.e. all the rows, columns and diagonals add to the same number. One or two pupils might be able to complete a magic square where one number is missing. To complete the square the pupil calculates $16 + 2 + 12 = 30$; $8 + 18 = 26$; $30 - 26 = 4$.

8	1	6
3	5	7
4	9	2

16	2	12
6	10	14
8	18	

22 Tables

The two and three times tables were considered in section 11 of Stage 3. Both the construction and the multiplication facts of the two times table should be revised. The same activities can then be carried out to construct the four times table, the five times table and the ten times table, e.g.

$$1 + 1 + 1 + 1 = 4 \qquad 4 \times 1 = 4$$
$$2 + 2 + 2 + 2 = 8 \qquad 4 \times 2 = 8$$
$$3 + 3 + 3 + 3 = 12 \text{ etc} \qquad 4 \times 3 = 12 \text{ etc}$$

Once the pupil is familiar with these multiplication facts, he might like to compare the 'stations' of the two times and the four times tables, i.e.

2	4	6	8	10	12	14	16	18	20
	4		8		12		16		20

When the pupil becomes familiar with the stations of the five and ten times tables they can also be compared in the same way.

23 Multiplication facts

Bingo cards for 'Four times', 'Five times' and 'Ten times' Bingo games should be made and used. Section 11 gives the rules of play. If a spinner is not available two dice, each marked 0 to 5, can be used and the two numbers added before multiplying by the appropriate 'table' number.

Here is a game to consolidate the multiplication facts of the two, three, four, five and ten times tables.

'Multiply and add' game
A pack of numeral cards for 1 to 10 should be used and a dice marked 1, 2, 3, 4, 5, 10. The pack of numeral cards is shuffled and placed face down in the centre of the table. Each player turns over the top unseen numeral card and throws the dice. The dice gives the multiplier and the numeral card the number to be multiplied. The answer to the multiplication is written down on the player's score card and added to the previous total. (The pupil will have to be told how to find '1 times' a number, i.e. the number itself.) The first player to gain a total greater than one hundred wins the game. The numeral cards can be shuffled and placed face down again when required.

24 Division
Sharing
In previous sharing activities the child is likely to have carried out the task by giving 'one to you, one to you' etc. It is now time for the child to begin to see this task in a new way and gradually be able to link such work to his knowledge of multiplication. If the child is asked to share fifteen blocks equally amongst three, he should be shown how to consider which number can be given to each share, e.g. the pupil can ask himself 'Can I give three to each share? Three threes are nine. Yes, nine is less than fifteen so I can give three to each share'. Thus the sharing can be carried out in steps, gradually working towards a one-step process where the child calculates the number to be given to each share and merely uses the materials to confirm his answer.

Repeated subtraction
In repeated subtraction activities, again the pupil should try to calculate the answer and then use the materials as a check, e.g. 'How many fours are twenty? Five fours are twenty'. Examples at this stage should be drawn only from the tables known to the pupil and no remainders should be involved. It is important to realize that in repeated subtraction examples the pupil is using his knowledge of the table of fours etc rather than the times tables.

25 Word problems
Problem arithmetic is so difficult because it depends on interpretation

and understanding skills which, in most instances, have not been taught.

Emphasis on understanding implies that problems of language occur right at the beginning of any new teaching section. Through the use of concrete materials, language is established to aid understanding and the mechanical example is an abstraction from this understanding. It is problems first, then the mechanical computation. This approach, however, leads to some difficulties, especially for the slow learner.

The use of materials, the opportunity to discuss with teacher and with classmates, and the experiences from games should have equipped the pupil with a good oral vocabulary for his mathematics but it is unlikely that he has a similar facility with written texts.

The teacher must realize that the reading challenge which mathematics worksheets, workcards and pages of text present to the slow learner must be met by teaching the mathematics vocabulary as new reading material. The teacher should constantly be asking herself, 'What are the words likely to present difficulty? What are the known words? Do the illustrations aid understanding of the longer sentences and more difficult vocabulary?' Reading lessons building on what the child knows, introducing new words with pictures and flash cards must be included as part of the mathematics lesson.

If the teacher makes up her own worksheets and workcards, she can use a large number of drawings, well-known vocabulary and only a few 'new' words. However, if using a commercial text, some pages present too many new words to be tackled by the pupil on his own and parts of the text put on tape by the teacher often provide the help a pupil requires.

Important vocabulary in addition and subtraction problems at this stage should include: add, plus, and, give, make, altogether, subtract, take away, minus, leaves, more, less, greater, smaller, difference between etc.

A workcard made up by the teacher for slow learners could look as shown opposite.

The pupil can revise the number names and learn any new words in the given list. The repetition in the three questions should also aid reading.

FRACTIONS
The pupil should be able to:
26   recognize, match and create fractions other than halves and quarters, e.g. thirds, fifths
27   record fractions, e.g. $\frac{1}{3}, \frac{2}{3}, \frac{3}{3}, \frac{1}{5}, \frac{3}{5}$

---

cakes, plate, pencils, box, sweets, jar, takes away, left

---

1  There are fourteen cakes on a plate.

 Ann takes away six of the cakes.

 How many cakes are left?

2 There are seventeen pencils in a box.
Bill takes away eight of the pencils.
How many pencils are left?

3   There are twenty-four sweets in a jar.
Mary takes away fifteen of the sweets.
How many sweets are left?

---

28 recognize 1 as $\frac{2}{2}$, $\frac{3}{3}$, $\frac{4}{4}$, $\frac{5}{5}$ 2 as $\frac{4}{2}$, $\frac{6}{3}$, $\frac{8}{4}$, $\frac{10}{5}$

29 recognize, match and create mixed fractions e.g. $\frac{11}{4}$, $2\frac{1}{2}$

30 create and recognize a family of the equivalent fractions $\{\,1, \frac{2}{2}, \frac{4}{4}, \frac{8}{8}\,\}$, $\{\,\frac{1}{2}, \frac{2}{4}, \frac{4}{8}\,\}$.

26 Fractional parts

Recognition and creation of halves and quarters should be revised. The pupil should then have the opportunity of making other fractional parts. Initially these tasks can be structured by the use of material such as squared paper. The pupil can be asked to cut a strip of paper (of say six squares) into squares and then asked questions such as: 'Into how many parts have you cut the whole strip? Are the parts equal? One out of six equal parts is called one sixth—show me one sixth. How many sixths have I put here? Colour four-sixths blue. How many sixths are un-coloured?' Activities aimed at giving experience in thirds and fifths can be carried out in a similar way.

The pupil can now tackle a less structured task. Ask him to fold a sheet of paper, once, twice and finally a third time. When the pupil opens out his sheet of paper he can be asked these questions: 'Are the parts equal? How many equal parts are there? What fraction of the whole sheet is one of these parts? What do you call five of these parts?'

The aim of this work is to establish what is meant by expressions such as one-sixth and three-eighths.

27 Fractional notation

The pupil will need not only to talk about his fraction work but also to record and label. Fractional notation for halves and quarters has already been met so this should be revised by perhaps using the domino game suggested in section 33 of Stage 2 (page 99).

Examples linking oral expressions to fractional notation, illustrated by a diagram, can be worked by the pupil.

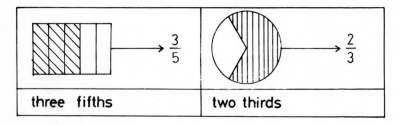

Displays of Cuisenaire rods can be made up by one pupil and labelled by another. The orange rod is used as one whole in these examples.

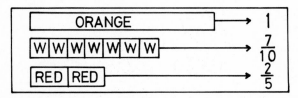

In these examples the pupil should match a number of a given rod to the orange rod and then record the value of the given display, e.g. ten white rods match the orange rod so the pupil should realize one white rod is one tenth and that seven white rods are seven tenths of the orange rod.

28 Whole numbers as fractions

The pupil can be given a set of equal strips of paper. Each represents one whole. One strip should be left untouched while the others are folded and cut into different fractional parts, e.g. halves, thirds, quarters, fifths and sixths. Folding to obtain thirds, fifths and sixths will probably require some help from the teacher in order to achieve equal parts.

By matching the equal cut pieces to the uncut strip, which is labelled one whole (1), the pupil can record one whole in different forms, i.e. one whole equals two halves, three thirds, four quarters etc or

$$1 = \tfrac{1}{1} = \tfrac{2}{2} = \tfrac{3}{3} = \tfrac{4}{4} = \tfrac{5}{5} = \tfrac{6}{6}.$$

Two children working together and putting their uncut strips and pieces side by side can find equivalent fractions for two wholes, i.e. two wholes equal four halves, six thirds, eight quarters etc or

$$2 = \tfrac{2}{1} = \tfrac{4}{2} = \tfrac{6}{3} = \tfrac{8}{4} = \tfrac{10}{5} = \tfrac{12}{6}.$$

29 Mixed fractions

The pupil can be given sets of equal sectors of a circle and asked to record the value of each set, as shown:

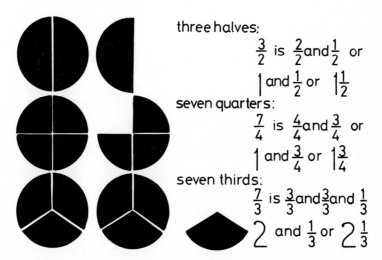

three halves:

$\tfrac{3}{2}$ is $\tfrac{2}{2}$ and $\tfrac{1}{2}$ or

1 and $\tfrac{1}{2}$ or $1\tfrac{1}{2}$

seven quarters:

$\tfrac{7}{4}$ is $\tfrac{4}{4}$ and $\tfrac{3}{4}$ or

1 and $\tfrac{3}{4}$ or $1\tfrac{3}{4}$

seven thirds:

$\tfrac{7}{3}$ is $\tfrac{3}{3}$ and $\tfrac{3}{3}$ and $\tfrac{1}{3}$

2 and $\tfrac{1}{3}$ or $2\tfrac{1}{3}$

When the children have been shown how to write and recognize mixed fractions they can work examples like these.

1   Colour $1\frac{1}{2}$ circles red

2   Colour $1\frac{1}{4}$ circles blue.

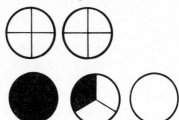

3   $1\frac{1}{3}$ of the circles are coloured.
How many are uncoloured?

4   Colour $1\frac{3}{4}$ of these shapes blue. Colour the other parts red. How much is coloured red?

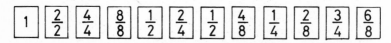

Mixed fractions can also be used when recording lengths to the nearest half or quarter metre, volumes, areas and weight to the nearest half or quarter of an arbitrary standard. More details of these activities will be given later in sections 37, 40, 41 and 43 of Stage 3.

30   Equivalent fractions

Most children find the concept of equivalence of fractions difficult and thus many examples using concrete materials are necessary.

The pupil has already met some equivalent examples, e.g. $1 = \frac{4}{4}$, and from matching materials he may be becoming familiar with others, e.g. $\frac{1}{2} = \frac{2}{4}$.

The pupil can be given four circles of paper (or strips if this is easier). One circle is left unfolded but the others are folded and cut to produce halves, quarters and eighths. The pieces should be labelled. Then by matching the pieces, the following equivalent values can be found and recorded: $1 = \frac{2}{2}$, $\frac{1}{2} = \frac{2}{4}$, $1 = \frac{4}{4}$, $\frac{1}{4} = \frac{2}{8}$, $\frac{1}{2} = \frac{4}{8}$, $\frac{3}{4} = \frac{6}{8}$, $1 = \frac{8}{8}$.

Game

A game of 'Fraction pairs' can be played. A set of twelve cards is marked like these:

1	$\frac{2}{2}$	$\frac{4}{4}$	$\frac{8}{8}$	$\frac{1}{2}$	$\frac{2}{4}$	$\frac{1}{2}$	$\frac{4}{8}$	$\frac{1}{4}$	$\frac{2}{8}$	$\frac{3}{4}$	$\frac{6}{8}$

The set of cards is shuffled and placed face down in three rows of four cards. Each player turns over any two cards. If the cards show equivalent values they are collected by the player. If the cards do not show equivalent values they are returned face down again. The player who collects most cards is the winner.

MONEY
The pupil should be able to:

31 recognize the 50p coin and match it to equivalent values, e.g. five 10p coins, twenty-five 2p coins, fifty 1p coins, three 10p and four 5p coins

32 show, recognize and record amounts 1p to 100p

33 add and subtract amounts of money within the range 1p to 100p

34 calculate the cost of several of the same articles (related to multiplication in the number work)

35 carry out some sharing and repeated subtraction activities with coins

36 give shopkeeper's change, i.e. complementary addition, with a variety of coins, for amounts less than or equal to 80p.

31   The 50p coin
Recognition and use of the 1p, 2p, 5p and 10p coins should be revised through shopping activities and games.

When the pupil meets the fifty-pence coin encourage him to feel the seven slightly curved edges and look at the face design.

There are numerous ways of showing fifty pence with 1p, 2p, 5p and 10p coins. Each pupil should try to find five different combinations of coins and then compare these with the sets of coins laid out by other class mates. If printed gummed-paper coins or coin stamps are available, the pupils can compile a book or display to illustrate the sets of coins. Each set can be labelled, e.g. 10p + 10p + 10p + 5p + 5p + 5p + 2p + 2p + 1p = 50p.

32   Amounts from 1p to 100p
The pupil can be given a set of cards, each of which shows a sum of money which the pupil has to lay out in coins, e.g.

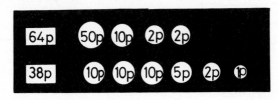

Shopping activities can be structured so that the pupil has a purse full of coins with which he can be asked to purchase an article by handing

over the exact amount. The pupil should participate in labelling items in
the shop so that he has the opportunity to write amounts in this money
range.

Domino game
A domino game would be ideal at this time. It is best to use seven
amounts and each is used seven times on twenty-eight cards, each of
which shows two numbers. The amounts used might be 5p, 10p, 25p,
50p, 63p, 78p and 89p. These amounts can be illustrated by coins, words
or numerals. Here are drawings to show some of the cards for such a
game:

33 Addition and subtraction of money
Although some written examples should be tackled by the pupil, the
emphasis will be on practical activities using coins. Opportunities will
arise to use real coins when the pupils are paying for school lunches,
making purchases at the school tuckshop, depositing money in the
school bank, contributing to charities or paying for outings. Classroom
activities can include selecting and paying for a meal, planning an outing
to a cinema and running a library. As well as giving practice in handling
coins and making calculations, such activities give scope for language
work, drama and art (posters, menus etc).

Game
Here is a game to give practice in adding and subtracting money. A set
of thirty cards are made out with instructions to 'pay' or 'collect'
amounts from 1p to 20p. Each player is dealt three cards by a banker.
The player looks at his three cards and selects the two which will give
him the greatest amount of money. These cards are placed face up in
front of the player and the other card is left face down. The banker asks
each player how much his cards are worth. The players are paid by the
banker. All cards are collected, shuffled and another round of the game
played. The first player to obtain more than 80p is the winner.

34 The cost of more than one
'A bag of sweets costs 8p. How much would four of these bags cost?'

The pupil presented with this problem either orally or illustrated on a workcard may tackle the calculation by repeated addition, i.e.

$$\begin{array}{r} 8p \\ 8p \\ 8p \\ +8p \\ \hline 32p \\ \hline \end{array}$$

The teacher can show the pupil that this calculation can also be a multiplication, $4 \times 8p = 32p$, where the pupil can use his knowledge of the multiplication tables.

35 Division

Sharing coins

It is interesting to observe how a pupil would share amongst three a set of mixed coins, e.g. one ten-pence coin, two five-pence coins and four one-penny coins. Through experience the pupil should find it easier to share the coins of greater value first, then if any are left, these can be exchanged for smaller coins and shared. If the pupil does not find this method of sharing for himself it can be shown to him like this:

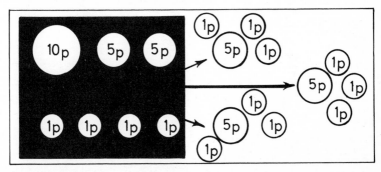

'One ten-pence coin cannot be shared. It is exchanged for two five-pence coins. Four five-pence coins to be shared. One five-pence coin is given to each share and one is left. It is exchanged for five one-penny coins. Nine one-penny coins to be shared. Three one-penny coins are given to each share'.

The pupil can record answers for the practical examples by filling in the amount shared, the number it was shared amongst and the amount of each share in sentences like these:

24p is shared amongst 3 . Each share is 8p .

Repeated subtraction activities with coins
'How many 2p coins are there in 16p?' This type of question can be
presented as a bag of mixed coins, e.g. one ten, one five and one penny,
to be changed into two-pence coins and then these are counted.

Answers can be recorded as:

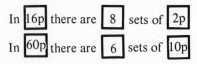

The known multiplication tables allow the pupil to tackle finding how
many two-pence, five-pence or ten-pence coins there are. The activities of
this section are an excellent background for the work in division in the
next stage of number development.

36   Shopkeeper's change

In section 32 it was suggested that in the classroom shop the pupil should
hand over the exact amount. Shopping should now require the
shopkeeper to give change to his customers.

Purses should be made up containing ten-pence and fifty-pence coins
for amounts 50p, 60p, 70p and 80p. The pupil collects one of these
purses, makes purchases in the shop and hands over a fifty-pence coin or
a number of ten-pence coins or a mixture of both coins, and the pupil
acting as shopkeeper gives the change by 'counting on'. Say the
purchases cost 37p. The customer hands over one 50p coin. The
shopkeeper counts the change using one-penny coins and a ten-pence
coin as '38p, 39p, 40p, 50p'. The shopkeepers will require a great deal of
practice to gain facility with a variety of coins.

MEASURE

In *length*, the pupil should be able to:
37   realize the need for a universal standard such as the metre
  estimate and find lengths to the nearest metre
  estimate and find lengths to the nearest half metre
  estimate and find lengths to the nearest quarter metre
38   realize the need for a smaller standard for measuring length such as
  the centimetre
  estimate and find lengths to the nearest centimetre.
In *volume*, the pupil should be able to:
39   secure the concept of conservation of volume, i.e. realize that
  matched volumes do not change when one or both are shown in a
  different form

40 express how much greater or smaller is the volume of one container or shape in comparison with another by using arbitrary standards.

In *area*, the pupil should be able to:

41 express how much greater or smaller is the area of one shape in comparison with another by the use of arbitrary standards.

In *weight*, the pupil should be able to:

42 secure the concept of conservation of weight i.e. realize that objects matched by weight do not change when one or both is changed in shape

43 express how much heavier or lighter one object is in comparison with another by the use of arbitrary standards.

In *time*, the pupils should be able to:

44 recognize, state and order the months of the year

45 recognize and show on the clock face half-past, quarter-past and quarter to hour times, e.g. half-past nine, quarter-past eleven, quarter to six

46 realize that there are
twenty-four hours in each day
seven days in one week
twenty-eight to thirty-one days, about four weeks, in one month
twelve months in one year.

37 The metre

The need for a universal standard

Through activities with arbitrary standards in Stage 2, the pupil should have been introduced to standards for measuring, such as rods, sticks, pencils and straws. He has gained experience in laying such sets of standards end to end along as straight a line as possible between the two points marking the distance to be measured. To emphasize the approximate nature of measurement the pupil has been encouraged to express answers in statements such as 'just over 5 rods long', 'between 6 and 7 sticks in length' and 'about 9 pencils'. When revising such work, the pupil should be encouraged to include fractional parts in his answers. Half and quarter standards should be included in the measuring sets and then answers might be 'about $4\frac{1}{2}$ sticks long' etc.

The early development of the measuring system relied heavily on body measurements as standards and the pupil should have experiences such as using his span, his foot, his step, his cubit (finger-tip to elbow) as measuring standards.

Activities using these are more difficult than activities using rods, pencils etc, because the pupil has to mark the distance covered by each span (or foot etc) and then count the marks. Two pupils working together will make the task easier and benefit from discussing what they are doing. Estimation and some simple questions involving computation should be included in the activities. Here is a suggested workcard:

Take chalk. Go to the car park.

1   How many steps long is the car?
2   Look at the front of the car.

3   How many steps do you think this distance will be?
4   Step along the front of the car. How many steps?
5   Did you think it was more steps or less steps?
6   How many steps longer is the side than the front of the car?

It may happen that two pupils working together obtain different answers for the same distance. Discussion can emphasize that one span, foot etc is likely to differ from one pupil to another and that the care taken when measuring can also vary.

Three pupils should each be given three different sticks, a garden cane, an unmarked ruler (about 30 cm long), a spill, and asked to measure the same distance, say the length of teacher's table. The pupils can record their results as shown opposite.

The pupils will realize that they cannot tell other people about measurements unless they all know the standard used. It should be explained that the standards which many of the people in the world use are metric standards. The basic standard used for measuring lengths is the metre.

Measuring to the nearest metre
The metre is too large a standard to measure many objects in the classroom. However, the child should carry out activities where he finds objects about a metre long, just over a metre in length and just under a

THE TABLE   John

John's measure is about 1 stick
Ann's measure is about 2 sticks
Jim's measure is about 6 sticks

metre in length. He can guess the length of such objects and then check his guess by using a metre stick.

Long distances such as the length of the corridor, the length of the school boundary, the distance from the school gate to the bus stop are sensible ones for the pupil to measure to the nearest metre. A trundle wheel can be used. The pupil should be shown how a length of string matched around the circumference of the wheel also matches the metre stick.

Measuring to the nearest half metre
When measuring shorter distances, a more accurate measure is required and so the pupil can be introduced to the half metre. A metre length of string or tape can be folded and the half marked. This length can be marked or noted on metre sticks, the tape and the trundle wheel. The child should also be reminded that two half metres make one whole metre. Measurements to be made to the nearest half metre can include the length and breadth of the school hall, the length of the frontage of the school building and the distance between two lamp posts.

Measuring to the nearest quarter metre
A metre length of string or tape should be folded into quarters and then one quarter, two quarters or one half, and three quarters can be marked or noted on metre sticks and tapes.

Tasks here can include measuring the width of the school entrance, the length of teacher's car, the length and breadth of the classroom and the length of the window ledge.

Recording results in this section of work should consolidate some of the concepts met in fraction work. The pupil should be encouraged to record two quarters as one half, thus applying his knowledge of equivalent fractions.

38 Introduction of the centimetre

Because of the unsuitability of the metre as a measuring standard for most classroom objects, the centimetre ought to be introduced at this point. The pupil should be shown a centimetre length (e.g. the unit Cuisenaire rod) and then asked to place a set of these end to end to match a metre length. In this way the pupil will discover that one hundred centimetres are the same as one metre. It can be explained that the name centimetre means one hundredth part of a metre. The pupil should try to find objects about a centimetre long.

Measuring to the nearest centimetre

The pupil can measure classroom objects and his own possessions to the nearest centimetre using at first a set of centimetre rods or cubes. He can then be shown how the ruler and tape have the centimetre lengths marked and numbered so that he can 'read' the result. The pupil should be given a wide variety of experiences in estimating and measuring straight and curved distances (e.g. around the wastepaper bin, a vase, and other containers) with rulers and a centimetre tape. Simple addition and subtraction of measured distances should be included in these activities.

Answers are expressed to the nearest centimetre. The pupil can record calculations in these formats:

$23cm + 28cm = 51cm$

$52cm - 27cm = 25cm$

cm	cm
31	72
+38	−43
69	29

39 Conservation of volume

There are various Piagetian tests devised to explore the pupil's concept of conservation of volume. These should be used to ensure that the pupil is ready to proceed to quantitative comparisons of volume.

40 Quantitative comparisons of volume

The pupil can now be asked to find not only if a container holds more or has a greater volume than another, but also to state in arbitrary standards how much more it holds.

Volumes of containers can be found and compared by using standards such as cups, spoons and jars. If water is not easily available, any pouring material (sand, salt, cereal) can be used.

Volumes of boxes can be expressed in terms of cube units, after having been filled with cubes. Here is a workcard for such a task:

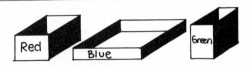

1　Guess which box holds most and which least.
2　Fill each box with cubes.

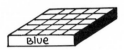

3　Write:
　　The red box holds about □ cubes
　　The blue box holds about □ cubes
　　The green box holds about □ cubes
4　Did you guess correctly?

From the activities in this section the pupil should realize that a standard for measuring volume fills space, i.e. that it is three-dimensional, that volume measurement like length is approximate, and that for sensible comparisons, estimates should be based on known volumes. The pupil continues to record answers using expressions such as 'about 6 cups', 'between 6 and 7 cups' and 'just over 6 cups'. He may also link this work to his knowledge of fractions and wish to state results as 'about $6\frac{1}{2}$ cups', 'nearly $6\frac{3}{4}$ cups' and 'almost $6\frac{1}{4}$ cups'.

41　Quantitative comparisons of area
Previously the pupil has been asked to compare areas by placing one surface on another or by making a perceptual choice. However, the example illustrated here demands another method of comparison:

Use of a set of arbitrary standards will allow the pupil not only to compare these areas but also to express the difference in area.

The pupil should experience a variety of arbitrary standards and different shapes, e.g. counters, triangles, rectangles, regular hexagons as well as squares. This could lead the pupil to stating a preference for some standards, e.g. circles don't fit together and leave spaces, while squares fit easily next to each other.

It is just as important that a variety of surfaces should be measured, not just those which are rectangular in shape, as it is that different sets of arbitrary standards should be used. Here is a suggested workcard:

Use cubes. Guess which shape has the greater area.
Measure both surfaces with the cubes.
Which has the greater area?
What is the difference between areas?

Answers in these activities are expressed to the nearest whole or fraction of a standard and the pupil can develop his own rules for calculating his results, e.g. he only counts whole standards inside the boundary of the shape; he counts whole standards and parts of standards which are greater than a half as wholes; he counts whole standards and tries mentally to match parts to form other wholes; he counts wholes and equates parts to halves or quarters.

42 Conservation of weight
There are various Piagetian tests devised to explore the pupil's concept of conservation of weight. These should be used to ensure that the pupil is ready to proceed to quantitative comparisons of weight.

43 Quantitative comparison of weight
The pupil should be trained to use the balance. Previously it was the teacher who checked to see if a balance was obtained when both pans were empty. The pupil can be shown how to check and adjust the balance before use. When using arbitrary standards, e.g. marbles, the

pupil has to decide how many of these give the best balance so that the weight of the object can be recorded to the nearest marble.

Here is a workcard to illustrate the type of activity which should be carried out by pupils, preferably working in pairs:

1   Balance the blue parcel with marbles.

2   Write:
    The blue box balances ☐ marbles.
3   Feel the red, green and yellow parcels.
4   Set out the parcels in order from lightest to heaviest.
5   Balance each parcel with marbles.
6   Write:

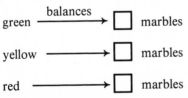

green ──balances──▶ ☐ marbles

yellow ─────────▶ ☐ marbles

red ─────────▶ ☐ marbles

7   Which parcels are heavier than the blue box?
8   How many marbles balance the four boxes?

The pupil should be using a large variety of arbitrary standards, e.g. cubes, beads, rods, cotton reels, chalk sticks, bottle tops, domino pieces, draughtsmen. The teacher should prepare a range of attractive parcels, each tested to make sure it can be placed on the balance pan and is balanced by a reasonable number (about ten to thirty) of the selected arbitrary standard.

Cuisenaire rods can be used as arbitrary standards and open up the possibility of half and quarter standards, e.g. if balancing a parcel with tan rods gives a result between nine and ten rods, a pink rod can be used as a half-rod and a red rod as a quarter-rod to give a more accurate result. The pupil can experiment with beads and cubes to find other half and quarter standards of weight for use in activities.

44 Months and seasons

The pupil should know the days of the week. He may already be familiar with the names of some of the months.

The calendar can be used to revise the names of days and to introduce the new interval of time, the month. This is a long period of time within the child's scale of reference. Each month name can be written on a card by the pupil. These cards can be used to help the pupil recognize and read the names as well as for ordering the months in sequence. The initial ordering should be from January to December. However, asking the pupil the question 'Which month comes before January?' will help him to realize that the sequence of months is continued over and over again.

45 Half past, quarter past and quarter to, hour times

Previously the pupil's attention has been concentrated on the small hand and hourly times, with the large hand fixed at twelve. The pupil is now shown how as the small hand moves from one number to the next, the large hand moves around the whole clock face. It is important that the child realizes that both hands are moving because recognizing and showing times on the clock face depends on the position of both hands. At half past, it is not only the large hand which has completed half its journey but the small hand also—it is half way to the next number. At half past three, the large hand has moved from twelve to six, i.e. half way around the clock face, and the small hand has moved half way from the three to the four.

A clock, perhaps an old one no longer in use, is best to show times. Here, unlike many teaching models, the movement of both hands is coordinated. If the pupil is shown drawings of the clock face or required to draw in hands on a worksheet of clock faces, he should be asked to discriminate between the hands by drawing them to specific sizes and to show clearly the position of each hand. Quarter past and quarter to are also identified through the position of both hands. The large hand is either a quarter way around the clock face or a quarter way from its return to twelve, while the small hand is a quarter of the way past one hour numeral or has only a quarter of the way to go to the next numeral. This section of work will benefit from a previous knowledge of halves and quarters.

46 Time relationships

The pupil has now met hours, days, weeks, months and seasons so it seems appropriate that he should be aware of the relationships between them.

1   The pupil does not always realize that a day is twenty-four hours long, i.e. it includes the time when he is sleeping. This can be illustrated by showing the pupil how the hour hand travels twice around the face of the clock each day. The small hand begins its second 'round' at midday.

2   One week is usually considered to be seven days in the order Sunday to Saturday, but the use of the expression 'a week today' should make the pupil begin to realize that one week is any seven days in sequence.

3   The rhyme 'Thirty days hath September' is still probably the easiest way of remembering the number of days in each month. However, for the slow learner the main teaching point is that all months do not have the same number of days. Most have thirty or thirty-one with February as the exception.
    Investigation of the calendar should make the number of days in each month something the pupil finds out for himself.

4   The pupil probably already realizes that there are twelve months in a year but he can be asked to find this information from the calendar. Although it is more difficult, the pupil may like to find out how many weeks are in one year from the calendar.

'Calendar Bingo' game

Some of the work in this section can be consolidated by the game 'Calendar Bingo'. Ideally, use the months from a calendar where each day has a clearly marked square. Unfortunately often squares are split to accommodate days in the fourth and fifth weeks, so cards for several months may have to be made up.

A set of instruction cards has to be compiled. The instructions could include: all the Mondays; any three days; one weekend; one Wednesday; 5th to the 9th; one week; all the Thursdays; any two days; first day.

The set of instruction cards is shuffled and placed face down in the centre of the table. Each player has one month which he uses as a Bingo card. A box of counters is also required. A player turns over the top unseen instruction card and uses counters to cover the required number of days. Some of the cards may provide discussion, e.g. one week can be taken as *any* seven days in sequence, a weekend is usually Saturday and Sunday (a *long* weekend may be included meaning Friday, Saturday, Sunday and Monday). If a day or days have already been covered, there is no need to do so again. The instruction cards should be shuffled and placed face down again whenever this is necessary. The first player to cover every day of his month is the winner.

SHAPE

The pupil should be able to:

47   describe the faces, edges, and corners of cubes, cylinders, cones, spheres, a square-based pyramid and a triangular prism

48   recognize and produce a set of two-dimensional shapes from the faces of three-dimensional shapes

49   recognize edges (or sides) and corners of two-dimensional shapes

50   establish relationships amongst two-dimensional shapes such as 'has as many edges as' and 'is the same shape as'

51   create in some form (Geoboard, Geostrips etc), recognize and sort rectangles, circles, triangles and squares

52   carry out simple symmetry activities e.g. paint blots, pegboard and squared-paper designs, cut-outs

53   carry out tiling patterns with rectangles, squares and equilateral triangles.

47   Faces, edges and corners of three-dimensional shapes

The pupil should know about the faces, edges and corners of three-dimensional shapes but he has probably not yet described specific shapes in terms of all three properties, e.g. a cube has six flat faces, twelve straight edges and eight corners. Although the pupil is tackling shapes in a new way, he may feel he has already covered this work and so the names of two 'new' shapes are introduced to add interest—a square-based pyramid and a triangular prism. The teacher is advised to use the proper mathematical names but the pupil may simply call these shapes 'a pyramid' and a 'chocolate packet' because he is thinking in terms of environmental examples of these shapes i.e. the pyramids of Egypt and the Toblerone packet.

After practice in describing each of the shapes, the pupil will enjoy playing these games.

The mystery bag

The pupils can play in threes. One player puts a shape into the bag, unseen by the other players. The second player feels the shape through the bag and describes its faces, edges and corners. The third player has to guess the name of the shape. Each player should have the opportunity of selecting a shape, stating the description and trying to identify it.

Edges, faces and corners

Here a pupil matches a shape to its name and properties. He is given a set of blank cards and writes them as labels as shown opposite. (For some slow learners, the teacher may decide to write the shape names and the words 'faces', 'edges' and 'corners', leaving the pupil to write in the appropriate number.)

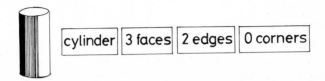

The pupil should make cards for the cylinder, sphere, cube, cuboid, cone, square-based pyramid and triangular prism.

48   Two-dimensional shapes

The pupil should realize that the faces of three-dimensional shapes are two-dimensional shapes. To produce such shapes the pupil can draw around the three-dimensional model onto a sheet of paper. However it is much easier, if they are available, to use a set of three-dimensional shapes with inset rubber edges which allow the pupil to use an ink stamp to obtain a stamped two-dimensional outline. Although by definition a two-dimensional shape cannot really be made in a concrete form for the pupil to handle, the expression 'flat shape' is used and so a shape with minimum depth or thickness is used by pupils at this stage in their mathematical development. Cartons can be cut up and the faces used as flat shapes. As he carries out this exercise, the pupil can find how many different shapes he can make from one carton, e.g. a triangular prism will give two different shapes, two faces are of one shape and three of another. The names of the shapes do not need to be mentioned at this time, although a pupil may volunteer the names he knows.

49   Properties of flat shapes

It is a matter of opinion as to whether the outline of the two-dimensional shape is referred to as edge or side—the name edge will be used here. Edges can be curved or straight and shapes have different numbers of edges and corners. The pupil can sort a set of flat shapes according to these properties.

50   Relationships

Arrow diagrams can tell 'stories' about the shapes, e.g. 'has as many edges as'.

The pupil can link a set of concrete flat shapes by using paper, card or plastic arrows.

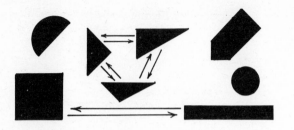

'has as
many
edges as'

51   Names of flat shapes

From the work of the previous sections the pupil will be aware of shared properties of some shapes i.e. that families of shapes exist. He can now learn the names of such families.

Shapes with three straight edges are called triangles. The pupil can sort the shapes with three edges from a set of flat shapes. He can make such shapes by using plastic strips joined by paper fasteners (Geostrips). He should be encouraged to use three equal strips, two equal strips with one shorter one and then with a longer one and finally three strips of different lengths. The three lengths must be such that the sum of any two is greater than the third. A nailboard or Geoboard can be the background for shapes formed by elastic bands (a square or triangular grid can be used or preferably both). The pupil should be encouraged to make as many different shapes with three edges as possible.

Here are a few of the triangles which can be formed:

Shapes on a square grid   *Shapes on a triangular grid*

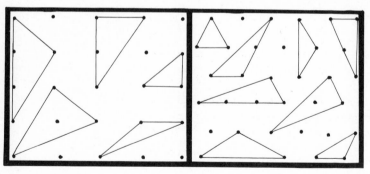

Shapes with four edges are called quadrilaterals. The pupil learns to identify two families of four-edged shapes. He is unlikely to know the name square and to be able to identify these shapes within a given set. When trying to make this shape with the plastic strips, the pupil will find that he requires four equal lengths. The strips have also to be held in a certain way to make the corners 'square'. The pupil should be shown that no matter which way he places a square on the table it retains the property of squareness, i.e. four equal edges and four square corners.

Another family of shapes with 'square corners' are the rectangles. Here opposite edges are the same length. The fact that a square is a special rectangle does not have to be mentioned to the pupil at this time, but care should be taken to avoid making statements which are not always true, e.g. a rectangle has two long edges and two short edges. Another shape, the circle, always looks the same no matter how it is placed on the table. This is another family the pupil should be able to recognize. The pupil can recognize circles, triangles, squares and rectangles in the classroom and out of doors.

52 Symmetry
Children like their drawings to have symmetry. A window in one side of a house is usually balanced by a window on the other side. The following activities can be described to the pupils as balanced patterns.

Pegboard
A balance line can be created on a piece of pegboard by placing a length of string around it as shown in this diagram. Either one side of the

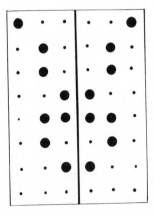

pattern is prepared by the teacher for the pupil to copy, or two pupils play 'Follow the leader'. One pupil puts in a peg on his side and the other balances this with an identical peg on his side. This is continued until the pattern is completed. The other pupil then has the opportunity to be the leader.

Squared paper

A balance line is drawn on a squared-paper grid. One side of the pattern of coloured squares can be prepared by the teacher (or a pupil) and then copied. The game 'Follow the leader' can also be played by colouring squares. Patterns can be simple or complicated, depending on the number of squares, the arrangement and the colours used.

Paint blots

This is not as easy as it looks. The paper used should not be too absorbent and the paint needs to be fairly thick. Place a blob of one or several colours of paint in the centre of the paper. There should be no attempt to paint or create a design. Fold the sheet of paper, preferably through the blob of paint. Stroke the outside of the folded sheet with your fingers to spread the paint on the inside. Open out the sheet of paper and leave the symmetric design to dry.

Cutouts

Fold a sheet of paper and then tear or cut-out a shape at the folded edge. Both the cut-out shape and the outline show a symmetric design.

The pupil should look out for symmetric designs on tiles, wallpaper and in pictures.

53   Tiling patterns

The pupil can be given a set of congruent (identical) squares and asked to fit them together. He can then investigate if other sets of a shape fit together without any spaces in the same way as the squares do. Circles do not fit together without spaces but rectangles and triangles do. (At this stage the pupil should be given a set of equilateral triangles.)

Rectangles provide the challenge of being fitted together in different ways. Here are some tiling patterns.

The pupils can also look at tiled patterns in the school, in the street and in their homes.

PICTORIAL REPRESENTATION
The pupil should be able to:
54 **construct and interpret data as a block graph, arrow diagram or table.**

54 Block graphs, arrow diagrams and tables

The slow learner can gain great satisfaction from pictorial representa-- tion, since data presented in this form cuts out reading difficulties associated with other forms of presentation. Throughout Stage 3 there are opportunities for presenting data in pictorial form and some of these have been mentioned, e.g. traffic and pupil tallies in section 5. In this section the development of the pictorial representation of data is continued and some suggestions are made for pictorial work which can be carried out at any time during Stage 3.

In a block graph the pupil represents one item of data by one square on the graph. In this example Jim kept a record of how many pages he read in his reading book during one week.

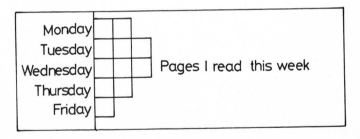

Discussion should take place about how well he did on Tuesday and Wednesday and suggest that he must keep up the effort. Did he go out or watch too much television on Friday night? Would he read on Satur- day and/or Sunday? The pupils can join together to produce information about types of pets, methods of coming to school, favourite TV programmes and favourite sweets etc.

Arrow diagrams can also be used. Data on favourite crisps follows:

Such diagrams are best kept to record information about a few things or people. If there are too many arrows, the message is not clear.

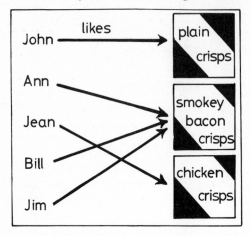

Discussion here could concentrate on who would want to know about people's favourite crisps and how much information could be collected. The data in the diagram can also be interpreted.

Information can often be recorded in a 'table', but children at this stage in their development find drawing the table difficult. Slow learners especially can put so much effort into drawing the table outline that any pleasure in the task is lost and the amount of time spent is out of proportion to the mathematics involved. The use of lined or squared paper, or even better, duplicated outlines, can overcome such difficulties.

Here is Bill's record of vehicles counted on his way to school.

DAY	NUMBER OF VEHICLES
Monday	14
Tuesday	8
Wednesday	23
Thursday	19
Friday	26
Total	90

Ann recorded weighing parcels in this table:

OBJECT	ESTIMATE	MEASURE IN CUBES	DIFFERENCE
tin	/////	12	/////
jar	16	20	4
box	8	6	2
packet	12	13	1

Discussion should always take place about the data. What does it tell us? Why was this in the table? Should we have included other items?

STAGE 4

Number
The number range is 0 to 1000. The six, seven, eight and nine times tables are included as well as multiplication by any number from zero to twenty. Division by a single digit is discussed, paying special attention to the language and the extended recording format.

Fractions
Fraction work is linked to the operation of division through finding fractions of quantities, i.e. $\frac{1}{4}$ of 12 metres.

Money
The pound is met as the equivalent value to 100p. The decimal point is used as a separator of £s and pence in recording and calculating.

Measure
The universal metric standards, the centimetre, the litre, the square centimetre, the kilogram and the gram are used in practical measuring tasks. Time is recorded to the nearest five minutes. Times are expressed as am or pm and in 24-hour notation.

Shape
A wide experience of properties of both three-dimensional and two-dimensional shapes will be gained through the activities in the shape sections.

Pictorial representation
Bar charts with a vertical scale are introduced.

Numbers 0 to 1000
The pupil should be able to:
1 recognize, name and identify as hundreds, tens and units, the numerals 101 to 1000
   reproduce the numerals 101 to 1000
   order sets, number names and numerals within the range zero to one thousand
2 add any two numbers where the sum lies within the range zero to one thousand

3 subtract any two numbers where these numbers lie within the range zero to one thousand

4 construct the six, seven, eight and nine times tables

5 multiply any number by 2, 3, 4, 5, 6, 7, 8, 9 where the product lies within the range zero to one thousand

6 divide any number by 2, 3, 4, 5, 6, 7, 8, 9 where that number is less than or equal to one thousand

7 recognize and create number patterns

8 multiply and divide any number by ten where the number and the answer lie within the range zero to one thousand

9 multiply any number by 11, 12, 13, 14, 15, 16, 17, 18, 19, 20 where the product lies within the range zero to one thousand

10 carry out calculations involving more than two numbers

11 recognize and name numbers greater than one thousand.

1 Numbers 101 to 1000

In Stage 4 numbers are an interpretation of place value rather than a label which states the cardinality of a set.

In section 16 of Stage 3 the pupil was shown how to make a notation card with columns for hundreds, tens and units. This card will be required for practice with the structured number pieces at this stage, e.g.

327 = ⎡3⎤ hundreds ⎡2⎤ tens ⎡7⎤ units = three hundred and twenty-seven

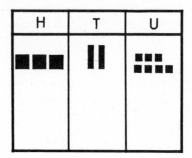

The pupil should be given exercises which ask him to:

1 discriminate between numbers such as 312, 213, 132, 123 etc
2 continue given sequences, e.g. 438, 439, —, —, —
3 find a number which is 1 less than, 2 more than, double etc a given number.

During such exercises the pupil can be asked 'Which number comes after 999?' and because of the pattern of numbers which has been established the pupil will probably be able to state 1000, giving the name one thousand, if he knows it. The pupil should be shown the block which represents one thousand in the number pieces and he can then check that this matches ten hundreds, one hundred tens and one thousand units. If there are enough tens and units this can be made into a practical exercise with several pupils counting and grouping the pieces in tens and then combining their pieces together.

The pupil should also have experience of hearing and saying the ordinal number names between the hundred-and-first and the thousandth even though use of such expressions is very limited.

2 Addition

For the new work in this section, it is suggested that examples be tackled initially using the structured number pieces in the following steps:

1   addition where no column has a total greater than nine, e.g. 324 + 3, 415 + 32, 626 + 153

2   addition where ten units are exchanged for one ten, e.g. 517 + 8, 98 + 4, 237 + 45, 165 + 319

3   addition where ten tens are exchanged for one hundred, e.g. 96 + 32, 243 + 71, 182 + 565

4   addition where ten units are exchanged for one ten and ten tens are exchanged for one hundred, e.g. 98 + 7, 85 + 76, 426 + 95, 338 + 288. Language should be built up as the pupil uses the number pieces, as in this example.

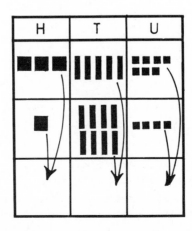

357 + 184 'Three hundred and fifty-seven is three hundreds, five tens and seven units. One hundred and eighty-four is one hundred, eight tens and four units. Seven units and four units are eleven units. Eleven units are one ten and one unit. Five tens and eight tens and one ten are fourteen tens. Fourteen tens are one hundred, and four tens. Three hundred and one hundred and one hundred are five hundreds. Five hundreds, four tens and one unit are five hundred and forty-one'.

5   addition to one thousand e.g. 800 + 200, 930 + 70, 993 + 7, 426 + 574.

The pupil will stop using material when he finds he can calculate more quickly without it and it can be emphasized that these are number bonds which the pupil already knows, i.e. as hundreds, but the pupil will realize that four and two make six whether it be units, tens or hundreds.

As well as working given examples, the pupil can create his own by using three packs of numeral cards on his notation board.

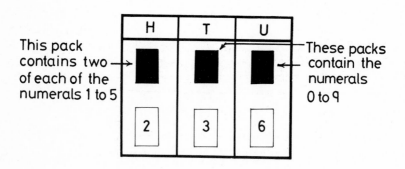

The three packs are placed face down in the positions shown in the diagram. The top unseen card in each column is turned over and the child records this as the first number to be added. The next set of top unseen cards is turned over and the child has the second number for his calculation. This number is also used as the first number for the next calculation and so on, e.g.

```
  147        350        236
 +350       +236       +
 ----       ----       ----
  497        586
 ----       ----
```

3 Subtraction

The following steps are suggested for the new work of this section:

1 subtraction where there is no decomposition of ten, e.g. $378 - 4$, $297 - 35, 649 - 218$
2 subtraction with the decomposition of one ten to ten units, e.g. $173 - 8, 251 - 26, 462 - 134$
3 subtraction with the decomposition of one hundred to ten tens, e.g. $347 - 63, 328 - 172$
4 subtraction with the decomposition of one hundred to ten tens and one ten to ten units, e.g. $301 - 7, 424 - 76, 713 - 256$. Examples with zeros may require particular emphasis as shown here. $403 - 28$ 'Four hundred and three is four hundreds and three units. I want to take away eight units but I can't. There are no tens to exchange. One hundred is exchanged to ten tens, one ten is exchanged to ten units. Eight units from thirteen units leaves five units. Two tens from nine tens leaves seven tens. No hundreds from three hundreds leaves three hundreds. Three hundreds, seven tens and five units are three hundred and seventy-five'.

H	T	U
■■ ■■		■■■

The pupil will find little difficulty with this type of example as long as he has plenty of practice with the structured number pieces.

5 subtraction from one thousand, with the decomposition of one thousand to ten hundreds, one hundred to ten tens and one ten to ten units, e.g. $1000 - 6, 1000 - 47, 1000 - 321$.

After working with the materials and recording the answer only, the pupil should then record each step in the use of the materials. Gradually he will find it quicker to use his knowledge of subtraction bonds.

Some work on the method of complementary addition is most worthwhile but the number of steps of computation should be carefully considered for the slow learner if he is to be successful.

One-step calculations could be examples like: $10 - 4$, $45 - 43$, $86 - 2$, $100 - 97$, $340 - 338$, $1000 - 990$. The pupil has to use his knowledge of the number bonds to be able to say '$\boxed{4}$ and how many make $\boxed{10}$?' The examples here are based on making-up to the next ten or thinking of numbers reasonably close in the counting pattern. The calculation $103 - 86$ would be worked as

86 and how many make   90? $86 + \boxed{4}\ =\ 90$

90 and how many make 100? $90 + \boxed{10}\ =\ 100$

100 and how many make 103? $100 + \boxed{3}\ =\ 103$

$$86 + \boxed{17}\ =\ 103$$

Most slow learners will find this difficult.

Game

Here is a game to give subtraction practice. A pack of numeral cards with four of each of the numerals 0 to 9 is shuffled. Each player is dealt six cards which are placed face up in front of him (see below). Each player subtracts the first number from one thousand, and the following numbers from each answer. This player's score card would look like this:

The player with the lowest final score gains one point. If a player cannot carry out a subtraction because the previous answer is too small, he is taken to have a final score of 0. If two or more players have the same final answer, they each gain one point. The first player to gain five points is the winner.

4   Multiplication tables

The new tables should be linked to the known tables. Revise the two times and the four times table facts and then work can begin on the eight times table. The pupil can build up the table with Unifix blocks, Cuisenaire rods and by colouring squares ($\frac{1}{2}$ cm size). The pupil can also calculate the table by repeated addition and this can then be written in the more traditional form, e.g.

$1 + 1 + 1 + 1 + 1 + 1 + 1 + 1 = 8$ $8 \times 1 = 8$
$2 + 2 + 2 + 2 + 2 + 2 + 2 + 2 = 16$ $8 \times 2 = 16$
$3 + 3 + 3 + 3 + 3 + 3 + 3 + 3 = 24$ $8 \times 3 = 24$

The two, four, and eight times tables can be compared by the pupil completing a table like this:

$\times$	1	2	3	4	5	6	7	8	9	10
2	2	4	6	8	10	12	14	16	18	20
4	4	8	12	16	20	24	28	32	36	40
8	8	16	24	32	40	48	56	64	72	80

Discussion of this table should reveal the following points:

1   All the multiples are even numbers.
2   Every second 'station' in the two times table is a station of the four times table; every second 'station' of the four times table is a 'station' of the eight times table; every fourth 'station' of the two times table is a 'station' of the eight times table.
3   The 'stations' for the two times table are multiplied by 2 (doubled) to become the 'stations' in the four times; the 'stations' in the four times table are multiplied by 2 (doubled) to become the 'stations' in the eight times table.

This could lead to the pupils presenting the eight times table in these ways:

$8 \times 1 = 2 \times 4 \times 1 = 2 \times 4 = 8$ $\qquad$ $8 \times 1 = 4 \times 2 \times 1 = 4 \times 2 = 8$
$8 \times 2 = 2 \times 4 \times 2 = 2 \times 8 = 16$ $\qquad$ $8 \times 2 = 4 \times 2 \times 2 = 4 \times 4 = 16$
$8 \times 3 = 2 \times 4 \times 3 = 2 \times 12 = 24$ $\qquad$ $8 \times 3 = 4 \times 2 \times 3 = 4 \times 6 = 24$

A set of 'Eight times' Bingo cards should be made and used by the pupils (see sections 11 and 23 in Stage 3).

The three times table should be revised and the pupil can then construct the six times table and the nine times in exactly the same ways as he derived the eight times from the two times and the four times tables.

The 'times wheel' (see section 11, Stage 3) is a good format for giving the pupil practice in the multiplication facts of a table.

The pattern of numbers in the 'stations' of the nine times table should be shown to the pupils: 9, 18, 27, 36, 45, 54, 63, 72, 81, 90. The units digit decreases by one each time and the tens digit increases by one. Addition of the two digits in each 'station' always gives a total of nine.

The seven times table is left until last because it is the most difficult set of multiplication facts to learn. As seven is a prime number, i.e. it is divisible only by itself and by one, it cannot be linked to any other table. The pupil should construct the table in Unifix blocks, Cuisenaire rods and squared paper.

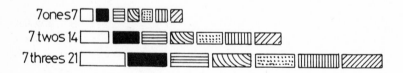

The table should also be calculated and recorded like this:

$1 + 1 + 1 + 1 + 1 + 1 + 1 = 7 \times 1 = 7$
$2 + 2 + 2 + 2 + 2 + 2 + 2 = 7 \times 2 = 14$
$3 + 3 + 3 + 3 + 3 + 3 + 3 = 7 \times 3 = 21$

The pupils should help to make and then use a set of 'Seven times' Bingo cards to help memorise these multiplication facts.

5   Multiplication by a single digit

Multiplication of or by zero has been left until now in the hope of making this difficult fact more meaningful. Examples should be tackled as other table facts are established, e.g. 4×0 means four zeros or $0 + 0 + 0 + 0$ and so the pupil can find the answer 0; 0×3 means no sets of three and so again the answer is 0. It is hoped the pupil himself will come to the conclusion that if one of the numbers in a multiplication is zero, then the answer is zero.

'Spot the answer' game

For this game a hundred square is required (see section 19, Stage 3), twenty counters for each player and a set of about twenty instruction cards, including items such as: 5×7; any four stations of 5; any number multiplied by itself; 6×3, 6×7, 6×4; 9×9; 7×6, 7×9; any three stations of 9; 8×1, 8×8, 8×3; any multiple of 2.

All the cards should be read through with the pupils before starting play to eliminate reading difficulties and explain new vocabulary such as 'multiple'.

The cards are shuffled and placed face down beside the hundred square. Each player turns over an instruction card and covers the appropriate number(s) on the hundred square with his counters. The first player with no counters left is the winner. The instruction cards may have to be shuffled and reused.

'Multiplication pairs' game

Each pupil should have two packs of numeral cards. Each pack, containing the numbers 0 to 10, should be shuffled and then the packs placed face down side by side in front of the pupil. Each player turns over the top unseen card from each of his packs. The player multiplies the two numbers together and the player with the highest answer wins a point. The first player to score five points is the winner. If necessary the packs are shuffled and used again.

'Highest score' game

The same packs of numeral cards which were used in 'Multiplication pairs' are required by each player. Each pack is shuffled and then dealt face up in columns. The pupil multiplies the numbers in each row and adds all the products together like this:

7	1
10	3
3	2
8	10
4	9

```
    7
  +30
  ───
   37
  + 6
  ───
   43
  +80
  ───
  123
  +36
  ───
  159 etc.
```

The pupil with the highest score wins the game. Each player's score can be checked by another pupil or by the teacher (with a calculator perhaps).

The pupil can fill out an 'operation table' which shows all the tables.

×	1	2	3	4	5	6	7	8	9	10
1										
2										
3										
4										
5										
6										
7										
8										
9										
10										

The slower learner might require help with the placing of the initial products. The symmetry of the table about one diagonal shows the commutative property of multiplication. This could be shown to the children as balance—they have tackled balance patterns in section 52, Stage 3. The pupil should then be asked to find a number, e.g. 7, in the table and then state which numbers multiplied together give an answer of 7. He should find 7 × 1 and 1 × 7 and after several examples like this he should realize that the order of the numbers does not matter in multiplication. It is then that the 'balanced pattern' of the table can be pointed out.

The teacher should point out that the numbers along the diagonal of the table (the balance line) are the results of multiplying a number by itself.

It is now possible to extend the pupil's knowledge of multiplication beyond the tables. To introduce this, the structured number pieces should be used in a repeated addition format for examples in the following steps.

1 Tens and units, then hundreds, ten and units multiplied by 2, 3 or 4 where no column has a total greater than nine, e.g. 3 × 31, 4 × 20, 2 × 43, 2 × 423, 3 × 132, 4 × 112. These examples should be worked in this way: 3 × 23 'Three threes are nine. Three two-tens are six tens. Six tens and nine units are sixty-nine'.

Examples can be recorded as

$$
\begin{array}{ccc}
31 & & 31 \\
\times\ 3 & & \times\ 3 \\
\hline
3 & \text{or} & 93 \\
90 & & \hline \\
\hline \\
93 \\
\hline
\end{array}
$$

The steps in the recording help the slower learner.

2   Tens and units, then hundreds, tens and units multiplied by 2, 3, or 4 where the exchanges of ten units for one ten and ten tens for one hundred are involved, e.g. 4 × 23, 3 × 42, 2 × 76, 2 × 426, 3 × 251, 4 × 165. An example of this type would be worked like this: 2 × 487 'Two sevens are fourteen. Fourteen units are one ten and four units. Two eight-tens are sixteen tens and one more ten makes seventeen tens. Seventeen tens are one hundred, and seven tens. Two four-hundreds are eight hundreds and one more hundred makes nine hundreds. Nine hundreds and seven tens and four units are nine hundred and seventy-four'.

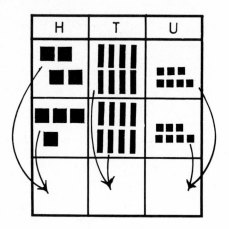

This example can be recorded as

$$
\begin{array}{r}
487 \\
\times\ 2 \\
\hline
14 \\
160 \\
800 \\
\hline
974 \\
\hline
\end{array}
\qquad \text{or} \qquad
\begin{array}{r}
487 \\
\times\ 2 \\
\hline
974 \\
\hline
\end{array}
$$

3   Gradually the pupil will not wish to use materials and then the range of multipliers can be extended to include 5, 6, 7, 8 and 9 which have been omitted until now.

Practice examples should be linked to school situations where possible, e.g. the number of attendances which could be made by a class in a week, ordering sets of workbooks and other equipment for pupils, the number of crisp packets in several boxes for the tuckshop. Some examples can be created by the pupil himself using two sets of numeral cards for 0 to 9 and a dice showing 0 to 9. The cards should be shuffled and two turned over at a time. The dice is thrown to give the multiplier:

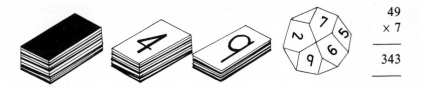

$$\begin{array}{r} 49 \\ \times 7 \\ \hline 343 \end{array}$$

To make sure that the pupil realizes that multiples extend beyond the 'stations' of the table, it is a good idea to look again at the hundred square. The pupil can be asked to cover with counters the stations of the two times table. He can then calculate products like these and be asked to cover these on the hundred square.

$$\begin{array}{ccc} 11 & 12 & 13 \\ \times 2 & \times 2 & \times 2 \\ \hline 22 & 24 & 26 \\ \hline \end{array}$$

$$\begin{array}{ccc} 21 & 22 & 23 \\ \times 2 & \times 2 & \times 2 \\ \hline 42 & 44 & 46 \\ \hline \end{array}$$

He should then begin to realize that all even numbers are multiples of two and see the alternate column pattern produced by the counters. Working in the same way by covering the stations, making some other calculations and then looking for a pattern, the sets of multiples of 3, 4, 5, 6, 7, 8 and 9 can be found.

The hundred square can also be looked at in another way. The pupil can be asked to cover the multiples of 2 with blue counters, then leaving these in position, the multiples of 4 can be covered with red counters.

This will again make the pupil think about the relationship between these multiples and show that the multiples of 4 are a subset of the multiples of 2. If the multiples of 8 are also covered with counters of another colour, these multiples will be seen to be a subset of the multiples of 4. Other relationships of multiples can be investigated.

6   Division by a single digit

1   Within the range of the tables

Equal sharing will be concentrated on in this section. The pupil can use materials but the emphasis at this time is on the relationship of division to the multiplication tables. $14 \div 2$ is interpreted as 'fourteen to be shared equally between two' and worked as 'two whats make fourteen? Two sevens make fourteen. Each share is seven'.

Initially the pupil should be restricted to one table. Examples can be filled in on worksheets with this layout:

$12 \div 2$ 2 sets of $\boxed{6}$ are 12 $12 \div 2 = \boxed{6}$

$20 \div 2$ 2 sets of $\boxed{}$ are 20 $20 \div 2 = \boxed{}$

A shorter form of recording can be adopted in time:

$24 \div 3$ $3 \times \boxed{8} = 24$ $24 \div 3 = \boxed{8}$

$18 \div 3$ $3 \times \boxed{} = 18$ $18 \div 3 = \boxed{}$

Then mixed examples can be used. A pupil may refer to copies of the tables initially but should be encouraged to manage without this help.

$63 \div 7$ $7 \times \boxed{} = 63$ $63 \div 7 = \boxed{}$

$30 \div 5$ $5 \times \boxed{} = 30$ $30 \div 5 = \boxed{}$

$24 \div 6$

$48 \div 8$

Gradually the pupil thinks through and records the steps himself. Remainders can be introduced when the child is showing success in the preceding type of example. Again one table at a time is used initially. This could be the format:

$17 \div 2$ 2 sets of $\boxed{8}$ and $\boxed{1}$ more make 17 $17 \div 2 = \boxed{8}$ r $\boxed{1}$

$11 \div 2$ 2 sets of $\boxed{}$ and $\boxed{}$ more make 11 $11 \div 2 = \boxed{}$ r $\boxed{}$

and then, when the pupil shows confidence in what he is doing, this shorter form:

$29 \div 3$ $3 \times \boxed{9} + \boxed{2} = 29$ $29 \div 3 = \boxed{9}$ r $\boxed{2}$

$19 \div 3$ $3 \times \boxed{} + \boxed{} = 19$ $19 \div 3 = \boxed{}$ r $\boxed{}$

Gradually the pupil adopts only the last step in this recording and is working with mixed divisors, e.g.

$65 \div 8 = 8 \text{ r } 1$ $36 \div 9 = 4$ $45 \div 6 = 7 \text{ r } 3$

A lot of practice is required with such examples because it is only when the child really copes with such work easily that he should move on to the next part of this section.

2   Tens and units divided by 2, 3 or 4 with no remainder

Here the structured number pieces are used. The method adopted is equal sharing. The language and recording established at this stage are used in all future division work and the pace should be matched to giving the pupil a sound foundation in understanding and manipulative ability. One divisor at a time should be tackled and examples carefully graded.

1   No exchange of a ten for ten units e.g. $82 \div 2$, $69 \div 3$, $88 \div 4$
2   An exchange of ten(s) for units e.g. $92 \div 2$, $45 \div 3$, $81 \div 3$, $56 \div 4$, $72 \div 4$.

Here is the how the example $68 \div 2$ would be worked. The calculation is interpreted as 'sixty-eight to be shared equally between two'. The sharing is best handled by beginning with the larger pieces, then if any are left, these can be exchanged for smaller pieces and then all the smaller pieces can be shared at the same time.

'Sixty-eight is six tens and eight units. Six tens to be shared equally between two. Two three tens are six tens, so each share is three tens.

Eight units to be shared equally between two. Two fours are eight s
each share is four units. Each share is three tens and four units, thirt
four'.

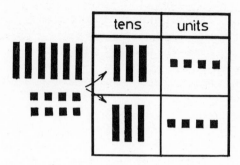

When the divisors 3 and 4 are used it is possible to have one, two an
three tens being exchanged for units. Most examples used should requir
only one ten to be exchanged for units and so make the handling c
materials easier. Most work at this point should be oral and concrete, bu
in time the pupil should record each step in the use of the materials lik
this:

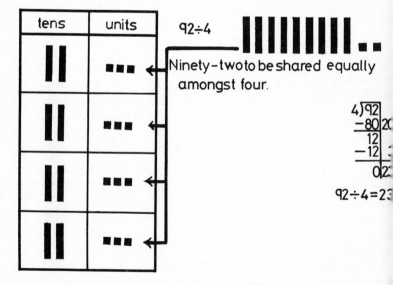

'Ninety-two is nine tens and two units. Nine tens to be shared equall
amongst four. Four two-tens are eight tens so each share is two tens an

ne ten is left. One ten is exchanged for ten units. Twelve units to be hared equally amongst four. Four threes are twelve so each share is hree units. Each share is two tens and three units, twenty-three'.

This language and recording format must be used with the materials therwise they don't make sense. When the pupil thinks 'nine tens to be hared' he must be thinking of nine ten-pieces not the number ninety. In he recording the answer is built up at the side. The subtraction sign is .sed to help the pupil understand the process. When the pupil uses the erm 'two tens' he writes 20 and 'eight tens' are recorded as 80. There is o 'crossing down' of numbers.

Hundreds, tens and units divided by 2, 3 or 4, with no remainder
The structured number pieces are used and in these examples the pupil ias to exchange hundreds for tens as well as tens for units. Examples hould be graded so that there is:

no exchange of pieces e.g. $246 \div 2$, $693 \div 3$, $844 \div 4$
an exchange of ten(s) for units e.g. $252 \div 2$, $972 \div 3$, $456 \div 4$, $868 \div 4$
an exchange of hundred(s) for tens e.g. $524 \div 2$, $456 \div 3$, $819 \div 3$, $520 \div 4$, $768 \div 4$
an exchange of hundred(s) for tens and ten(s) for units e.g. $734 \div 2$, $762 \div 3$, $528 \div 3$, $972 \div 4$, $668 \div 4$.

Again the teacher is advised not to give examples where the exchanges nvolved make the handling of the materials too laborious. Thus numbers vhere two or three hundreds are exchanged for tens and two or three ens are also exchanged for units should rarely be included. An example n this part of the division development would be worked like this: 468 ÷ 3 'Four hundred and sixty-eight is four hundreds, six tens and ight units. Four hundreds to be shared equally amongst three. Three ne-hundreds are three hundreds so each share is one hundred and one undred is left. One hundred is exchanged for ten tens. Sixteen tens to be hared equally amongst three. Three five-tens are fifteen-tens so each hare is five tens and one ten is left. One ten is exchanged for ten units. ighteen units are to be shared equally amongst three. Three sixes are ighteen so each share is six. Each share is one hundred, five tens and six nits, one hundred and fifty-six'.

It can easily be understood in examples like this why the larger pieces hould be shared first. All recorded calculations in addition, subtraction nd multiplication have emphasized beginning with the units. Don't ask hildren to dispense with this approach without a good reason. However,

	H	T	U

```
 3)468
  -300  100
   168
  -150   50
    18
   -18    6
     0  156
468÷3=  156
```

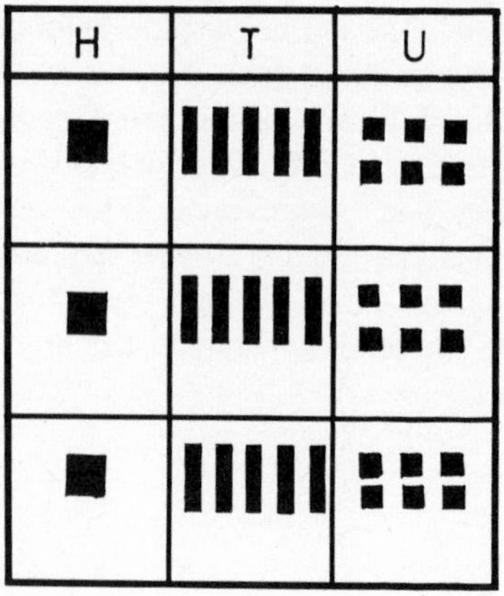

this use of materials provides a good reason for beginning at the left-hand side in the recording of a division calculation.

4   Tens and units; hundreds, ten and units, divided by 2, 3 or 4 with a remainder

$979 \div 4$ 'Nine hundred and seventy-nine to be shared equally amongst four. Nine hundreds to be shared equally amongst four. Four two-hundreds are eight hundreds, so each share is two hundreds and one hundred is left. One hundred is exchanged for ten tens. Seventeen tens to be shared equally amongst four. Four four-tens are sixteen tens, so each share is four tens and one ten is left. One ten is exchanged for ten units. Nineteen to be shared equally amongst four. Four fours are sixteen so each share is four and three are left. Each share is two hundreds, four tens and four units,·two hundred and forty-four, and the remainder is three'.

```
 4 )979
  -800  200

   179
  -160   40

    19
  -  16    4

     3  244
```

$979 \div 4 = 244r3$

5   *Tens and units; hundreds, tens and units, divided by any single digit, with and without a remainder*

Only when the child no longer requires the use of the structured materials and has developed a facility in understanding and recording at the earlier steps should he proceed to this work. It is impractical to use materials here, except for the occasional demonstration, because of the larger divisor. The language developed through the use of materials should continue to be used and the child should still use the expanded recording format, e.g.

$$
\begin{array}{r|r}
7\,\overline{)\,952} & \\
700 & 100 \\
\hline
252 & \\
210 & 30 \\
\hline
42 & \\
42 & 6 \\
\hline
& 136
\end{array}
$$

$$952 \div 7 = 136$$

After working many examples the pupil might adopt the more traditional recording of $7\overline{)9^2 5^4 2}$ with 136 above. This should not be rushed and perhaps not attempted at all by many slow learners.

7   Number patterns

The aims of this section are to give children the opportunity of handling numbers in the range zero to a thousand, to have practice in addition, subtraction, multiplication and division and combinations of these operations and to let the pupils enjoy creating their own number patterns.

The pupils can be given the first and second numbers and then be asked to create a pattern by following certain instructions, e.g.

1   Add 18 to each number to get the next five numbers in this series
    101, 119, —, —, —, —, —

2   Subtract 11 from each number to get the next five numbers in this series 999, 988, —, —, —, —, —

3   Multiply each number by 3 to get the next five numbers in this series
    1, 3, —, —, —, —, —

4   Divide each number by 2 to get the next five numbers in this series
    832, 416, —, —, —, —, —

5   Multiply by 2 and add 1 to each number to get the next five numbers
    in this series 9, 19, —, —, —, —, —
    What do you notice about the numbers you have written?
6   Subtract 1 and then divide by 3 to get the next four numbers in this
    series 607, 202, —, —, —, —

8   Multiplication and division by 10

Ask the pupil to write out the ten times table. A demonstration should be
carried out with a few examples of tens and units multiplied by ten using
the structured number pieces, e.g. 10×31. Three tens and one unit are
laid out ten times. The unit pieces are collected together. 'Ten ones are
ten'. The ten unit-pieces are exchanged for one ten. The ten pieces are
collected together. 'Ten three-tens are thirty-tens and one ten more is
thirty-one tens'. The thirty tens are exchanged for three hundreds. 'Three
hundreds, one ten and no units are three hundred and ten'. The answer is
recorded $10 \times 31 = 310$.

After a few examples, ask the pupil if he notices anything about the
number which is multiplied by ten and the answer. The pupil should find
the required relationship. The pupil and the teacher together can make a
'rule' for easy multiplication by ten. To emphasize the place-value aspect,
the pupil should be encouraged to use words like, 'Units become tens and
tens become hundreds when you multiply by ten'.

The pupil should now write down the answers (no calculation is required, just the use of the rule) to a selection of examples involving units,
and tens and units. The highest number which can be included is 100.

A few examples of division by ten should initially be worked by using
the structured number pieces and the expanded recording. The number
to be divided should have no units to avoid a remainder at this time, e.g.
$320 \div 10$. 'Three hundred and twenty to be shared equally amongst ten'.
The pieces are laid out to represent three hundred and twenty. Three
hundreds cannot be shared so the pieces are exchanged for tens. Three
tens are given to each share. The two tens cannot be shared so the pieces
are exchanged for units. Three tens and two units, thirty-two. This
answer is recorded:

$$
\begin{array}{r|r}
10 \,\overline{)\,320} & \\
300 & 30 \\
\hline
20 & \\
20 & 2 \\
\hline
 \quad\quad 0 & 32 \\
\end{array}
$$

$320 \div 10 = 32$

The relationship between the quotient and the dividend will probably be quickly recognized by the pupil. Again the pupil and teacher should construct a rule, e.g. 'Hundreds become tens and tens become units when you divide by ten'.

The pupil will now be keen to record some answers to examples. Allow him to work examples like these: $410 \div 10$, $30 \div 10$, $170 \div 10$, and then include an example with a units digit, e.g. $36 \div 10$. It will be interesting to see how he tackles this. If he has difficulty he should be given the number pieces to share and encouraged to show the full recording:

$$
\begin{array}{r|r}
10 \;) \; 36 & \\
30 & 3 \\
\hline
6 & 3
\end{array}
$$

$$36 \div 10 = 3 \, r \, 6$$

The pupil may have to carry out other examples but in time he should be able to amend his 'rule' to read something like this, 'Hundreds become tens, tens become units and units become the remainder when you divide by ten'. The pupil can now work mixed examples giving practice in multiplying and dividing by ten.

9 Multiplying by numbers 11 to 20
Now that the pupil knows how to multiply by ten, he can consider how to multiply by two tens.

$$20 = 10 \times 2 \qquad 20 \times 3 = 10 \times 2 \times 3 = 10 \times 6 = 60$$
$$20 \times 7 = 10 \times 2 \times 7 = 10 \times 14 = 140$$
$$20 \times 9 = 10 \times 2 \times 9 = 10 \times 18 = 180$$
$$20 \times 10 = 10 \times 2 \times 10 = 10 \times 20 = 200$$

In these examples the pupil uses his knowledge of the two times table and then his rule for multiplication by ten. For multiplication of numbers greater than ten the pupil could use this form of recording:

$$
\begin{array}{cc}
20 \times 36 & \begin{array}{r} 36 \\ \times 2 \\ \hline 72 \\ \times 10 \\ \hline 720 \\ \hline \end{array}
\end{array}
\qquad
\begin{array}{cc}
20 \times 48 & \begin{array}{r} 48 \\ \times 2 \\ \hline 96 \\ \times 10 \\ \hline 960 \\ \hline \end{array}
\end{array}
$$

The pupil will probably realize that it is almost a waste of time to write the second step and it can be suggested that he does both steps together, i.e. multiply by two but also move the answer digits one column to the left to make them ten times greater, e.g.

$$20 \times 17 \qquad \begin{array}{r} 17 \\ \times\ 20 \\ \hline 340 \\ \hline \end{array}$$

After these examples it is interesting to give the child a calculation such as 14 × 23 to discover how he would tackle it. He might try repeated addition, i.e. 23 added fourteen times or multiplication by factors, e.g. 2 × 7 × 23. The pupil will have to be introduced to the traditional method of distributing the multiplication over addition in which one of the numbers is ten, e.g. 17 × 32 would be worked as (10 + 7) × 32 = 10 × 32 + 7 × 32. The pupil would record this as:

$$\begin{array}{rrr}
32 & 32 & 320 \\
\times\ 10 & \times\ 7 & +\ 224 \\
\hline
320 & 224 & 544 \\
\hline
\end{array}$$

After some practice in recording the multiplication like that, the pupil can be shown a shorter recording:

$$\begin{array}{rr}
32 & 32 \\
\times\ 17 & \times\ 17 \\
\hline
224 & 320 \\
320 & 224 \\
\hline
544 & 544 \\
\hline
\end{array}$$

It does not matter whether the pupil multiplies by the ten first or by the seven first. If possible let the pupil decide which he would like to do and then he can always use that procedure.

Calculators are of tremendous use, especially to the slow learner, but the pupil must be taught how to use one. The calculator's accuracy is wholly dependent on the operator's skill in recognizing when he has perhaps fed in a wrong number or that the machine is malfunctioning.

10   Calculations with more than two numbers

In Stage 3 the pupil considered the addition of several numbers and calculations where there was a mixture of addition and subtraction, e.g. 142 + 621 + 81 and 32 − 11 + 9. The pupil had to realize that he could only handle two numbers at a time, find an answer and then combine this with the next number. It was also brought to the pupil's attention that the sign in front of the number states the operation which applies to it.

11 Numbers greater than one thousand
The pupil will be aware that there are numbers greater than one thousand through his calculations and games. It is perhaps now possible to begin to generalize about the place-value structure.

Column headings so far have been *thousands, hundreds, tens, units* and so it will be easy for the pupil to extend these to *tens of thousands* and *hundreds of thousands*. The next place value is millions and this new name would have to be introduced to the pupil. It is very difficult for pupils to understand such a large number and is probably best done as multiples of known quantities.

Pupils can be introduced to the idea that there is no largest number but that we can write a number as large as we have space to do so.

Exercises in writing and naming numbers should not extend beyond one million. The pupil can work with one set of numeral cards 0 to 9 and see how many numbers he can form using three cards, four cards and five cards, e.g. cards showing 3, 2, 6 would produce 326, 362, 236, 263, 632, 623 i.e. six numbers; cards showing 1, 7, 2, 5 would produce 1725, 1752, 1275, 1257, 1572, 1527, 2715, 2751, 2157, 2517, 2571, 5721, 5712, 5172, 5127, 5271, 5217, 7125, 7152, 7251, 7215, 7512, 7521 i.e. twenty-four numbers.

The slow learner will have difficulty in producing so many combinations, but he can be helped if the teacher suggests that he move only one card at a time. If the pupil has managed to work through three- and four-card numbers, ask him to estimate the number he can make up with five digits. He will then require help to find some of the one hundred and twenty different combinations.

FRACTIONS
The pupil should be able to:
12 calculate one half, one third, one fifth and one tenth of a given quantity.

12 Fractions of given quantities
The pupil has met fractional parts of one whole in the previous stages. In

this section he is introduced to fractional parts of whole numbers greater than one. As a link with previous work, it is suggested that counters, or blocks, are laid out in an array which can be physically halved, quartered etc. $\frac{1}{2}$ of 8 is found to be 4 by halving the rectangular array.

Other examples can be set out as shown in these diagrams:

$\frac{1}{3}$ of 15 = 5 $\frac{1}{4}$ of 12 = 3 $\frac{1}{5}$ of 20 = 4

During these activities the pupil may realize that to find one half is sharing equally between two, to find one third is sharing equally amongst three etc. This knowledge allows the pupil to calculate the required fraction by the process of division, e.g. $\frac{1}{4}$ of $20 = \frac{20}{4} = 5$. 'One quarter of twenty is twenty shared equally amongst four. Four 'whats' make twenty? Four fives make twenty. One quarter of twenty is five'. Examples should include measures, e.g.

$\frac{1}{3}$ of 9 metres $= \dfrac{9 \text{ metres}}{3} = 3$ metres

$\frac{1}{10}$ of 70 litres $= \dfrac{70 \text{ litres}}{10} = 7$ litres

MONEY
The pupil should be able to:
13   recognize the £1 note and match it to equivalent values of coins, e.g. one hundred 1p coins, ten 10p coins, twenty 5p coins, fifty 2p coins, two 50p coins, one 50p four 10p and ten 1p coins
14   show, recognize and record amounts within the range 1p to £10. The decimal point is regarded at this stage as a separator of £s and pence
15   add, subtract, multiply and divide amounts of money within the range 1p to £10

16   give the shopkeeper's change (i.e. complementary addition) with a
variety of coins, for amounts less than, or equal to, £4.

13   One pound

The pupil should have the opportunity of looking at one pound notes
(there are three issued by the Scottish banks and one issued by the Bank
of England). The design can be commented upon and the statement
'promise to pay' discussed. Plastic coins should be used to show as many
sets as possible of different coins for the equivalent value of £1.

A competition can be organized to find which pupil can find the
largest number of different sets.

14   Amounts from 1p to £10

Amounts greater than one pound can be laid out in coins and pound
notes. The pupil can also show the equivalence of various combinations:

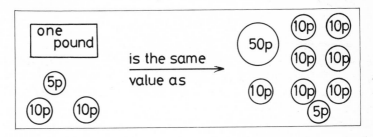

When the pupil is naming such amounts of money he can say 'one
pound twenty-five', or 'one hundred and twenty-five pence (or p)'. Either
the name pound or pence is used, not both. This practice is also used
when recording. The pupil writes £1.25 or 125p. The point is introduced
to and used by the pupil as a separator of pounds and pence at this stage.

Shopping activities have been suggested at all previous stages and no
exception is made here. However, the time seems ripe to renew interest
through making the classroom shop take another form. Because of the
measurement work at this stage, and the range of money suggested, a
'Do-it-yourself' shop would be ideal. Pupils should collect and bring
empty paint tins, ends of rolls of wallpaper, ceiling, carpet and lino tiles
to act as samples. Off-cuts of shelving, beading, formica can be begged
or borrowed and leaflets on self-assembly bookcases, small tables and
other items of furniture can be used for display and costing.

The pupils can label the paint tins and other items with prices
researched in local shops. Shopping should initially require the pupil to
purchase one item and pay for it using pound notes and coins. The pupils

will require some practice in counting out these larger amounts as this is a new experience for most of them.

When a pupil is finding it easy to lay coins and notes correctly for a given amount, he should be set the task of laying out specific values with as few coins as possible and recording these in his jotter, e.g.

£1·67 £1 (50p) (10p) (5p) (2p)
£1 + 50p + 10p + 5p + 2p = £1· 67

15   Money calculations

Calculations should be carried out in pence in the first instance, e.g. addition would be recorded like this:

```
      51p          and this  102p
      35p                     36p
    +43p                     124p
    ─────                    ─────
     129p ──────→ £1.29      262p ──────→ £2.62
    ─────                    ─────
```

Such addition work can occur as the result of purchases in the 'Do-it-yourself' shop, from the choice of food on a menu or from the selection of items in a catalogue etc. The pupil will also learn to record and work such calculations in pounds, e.g.

$$£1.25$$
$$+£3.63$$
$$─────$$
$$£4.88$$

When working in pounds, items of less than £1 should be recorded with a zero in front of the point or separator, i.e. 85p would be written as £0.85.

Subtraction calculations can arise from deductions made on items in the shop, a returned article subtracted from a bill or when finding the amount saved by comparing sale price with previous price etc. Again initially calculations should be carried out in pence, e.g.

£1.16 − 82p = 116p − 82p = 34p

£3.21 − 78p = 321p − 78p = 243p = £2.43

£4.31 − 93p   £4.31 ↠ 431p

```
              431p
             −93p
             ─────
              338p ──────→ £3.38
             ─────
```

Later the pupil will also learn to work in pounds:

£4.06	£3.46
−£1.32	−£0.87
£2.74	£2.59

Multiplication calculations can be related to finding the weekly cost of milk, papers etc, as well as from purchases of several items at the same price in the shop. Recordings can take these formats:

26p
×7

182p→£1.82

8p
×15

40
80

120 →£1.20

£1.62
×3

£4.86

Division work involves both equal sharing and repeated subtraction. Although the method taught for division was based on sharing, the pupil can be shown that the method is suitable for all division work. While shopping, division calculations are unlikely unless the shopper wants to find out how many of an article can be bought with the cash he has available. Equal sharing calculations may arise from the shared winning of a prize in a game. Here are some examples of division work:

1   £4.62 is to be shared equally amongst three boys. How much does each get?

£4.62 → 462p

$$3 \overline{)462}$$

300   100p

162
150   50p

12
12   4p

0   154p→ £1.54

Each share is £1.54

2   Mrs Brown has £8.32 in her purse. How many wall tiles at 7p each can she buy?

£8.32 → 832p

```
7 ) 832
    700 | 100
    ───
    132
     70 | 10
    ───
     62
     56 | 8
    ───
      6 | 118
```

She can buy 118 tiles. (She has 6p left in her purse.)

'Win, lose or chance' game

A game which takes time to make but gives the pupil so much fun and practice in money calculations that it is worthwhile, is 'Win, lose or chance'. The pupils can help to make the required equipment. A board showing a track of squares each coloured green, red or blue could look like this:

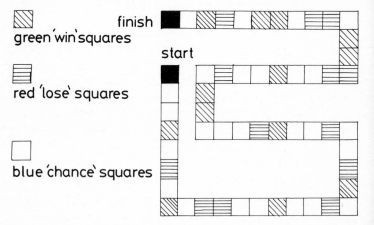

green 'win' squares

red 'lose' squares

blue 'chance' squares

finish

start

Three packs of cards are required. 'Win' cards denote amounts of money to be collected e.g. 35p, £1.09p, 3 × 16p, 82p ÷ 2. These amounts can be shown in words, numerals or by pictures of coins. 'Lose' cards indicate amounts of money to be paid to the bank, e.g. one pound ten, half of sixty-two pence, the sum of sixteen pence, eighteen pence and twenty pence. Again amounts can be expressed in words, numerals or by using gummed paper coins. Some cards in both the win and lose packs should give an option e.g. 'Pay £1 or take a chance card', 'Collect 3p or take a chance card'. 'Chance' cards have a mixture of penalties and rewards, e.g. 'Collect £1.09', 'Pay 82p', 'Lucky you—nothing to pay', 'Give each player 15p', 'Collect 20p from each player'.

Each player in turn moves a counter along the track according to the throw of a dice. When he stops in a square he takes an instruction card of the correct type—win, lose or chance according to the colour of the square—and pays or collects from the bank. When all players have crossed the finish line, the richest player is declared the winner.

16   Shopkeeper's change

Customer cards should be issued to pupils so that they have to buy things in the class shop for which they do not have the exact amount of money.

The teacher should act as shopkeeper at first and then let each pupil take turn. The shopkeeper gives change by 'counting on' e.g. the customer buys a tin of paint costing £2.39p and hands over £3 in payment. The shopkeeper gives coins in change like this, 'Two pounds thirty-nine, two pounds forty, two pounds fifty, three pounds'. Pupils will require a great deal of practice before they will handle the coins accurately, with confidence, and using as few coins as possible. Here is a game for three pupils to give practice in giving change.

'Pay-up' game

A pack of cards stating amounts of money in the range of 80p to £3.80p should be made up. (Most amounts should have the pence stated in the range 70 to 99p so that payment tends to require change.)

One pupil acts as the banker and has a supply of coins. The other pupils are each given ten one-pound notes. The amount cards are placed face down on the table. Each of the two players in turn places an amount card face up. On each occasion the required amount is paid to the banker. If change is required the banker gives this to the player by 'counting on'. The first player with no money left is the winner. Three rounds of this game should be played so that each pupil has a chance to be the banker.

MEASURE
In *length,* the pupil should be able to:
17   express his personal measurements to the nearest centimetre
18   add, subtract, multiply, and divide centimetre and metre lengths.
In *volume,* the pupil should be able to:
19   realize the need for a universal standard such as the litre
      estimate and find volumes to the nearest litre, half litre and quarter litre.
In *area,* the pupil should be able to:
20   realize the need for a universal standard such as the square centimetre
      estimate and find areas to the nearest square centimetre.
In *weight,* the pupil should be able to:
21   realize the need for a universal standard such as the kilogram
      estimate and find weights to the nearest kilogram, half kilogram and quarter kilogram
      realize the need for a smaller standard for greater accuracy in expressing weight e.g. the gram
      estimate and find weights to the nearest 20g.
In *time,* the pupil should be able to:
22   read and record the time to the nearest five minutes
23   understand and use the expressions am and pm
24   recognize and record hourly times as am or pm and in 24-hour notation.

17   Personal measurements
The pupils enjoy making and recording their personal measurements. The recording, to the nearest centimetre, can be on a chart. Two pupils working together can help each other to make the required measurements.

Children can make and compare measurements, e.g.

1   Measure from finger-tip to finger-tip. Is this a greater or smaller measurement than your height? What is the difference?
2   Is your ankle thicker than your wrist? What is the difference?

The pupils can compare their measurements with clothing sizes. 'Which centimetre lengths correspond to which shoe size?' This in-

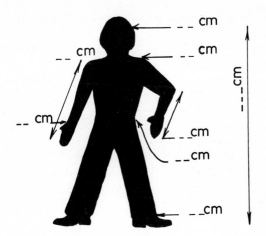

vestigation of length of foot and size of shoe can form the basis of an interesting discussion.

Many clothing labels are marked with chest, neck or waist size in centimetres so that these can be compared by the wearer with his own measurements. Other methods of sizing can be related to a range of centimetre measurements.

'Making a metre' game

This game involves measuring and computation. A pack of instruction cards are required. These state short lengths to be measured to the nearest centimetre, e.g.

Each player turns over a card from the pack, which has been placed face down in the centre of the table, and makes the required measurements with a centimetre tape. The result is noted on a score sheet and added to any previous measurement. The first player to make a metre i.e. record a total score of over 100 cm, is the winner. The instruction cards may have to be shuffled and used again.

18   Computation of lengths

Addition of centimetre lengths occurred in the game 'Making a metre'. Computation may arise when considering the materials required in craft work and calculations should also be written into measuring assignments. Here are some examples.

1   Measure each of the window ledges in the classroom. Find the total length of wood which was required to make all the ledges. Give your answer in centimetres and in metres and centimetres. Possible solution is:

$$
\begin{array}{r}
\text{cm} \\
127 \\
154 \\
+215 \\
\hline
496 \\
\hline
\end{array}
$$

The total length is 496 cm or 4m 96 cm.

2   Measure a shelf in the cupboard. What length of wood is required to make three of these shelves? Possible solution is:

$$
\begin{array}{r}
\text{cm} \\
172 \\
\times \quad 3 \\
\hline
516 \\
\hline
\end{array}
$$

516 cm or 5 m 16 cm is required.

3   Measure the edge of the window ledge. What length from a 2 metre strip will be left after you have fitted edging along the window? Possible solution is:

2m ⟶ 200cm

$$
\begin{array}{r}
\text{cm} \\
200 \\
-131 \\
\hline
69 \\
\hline
\end{array}
$$

69cm is left.

19   A universal standard of volume—the litre

In practical activities in the Stage 3, the pupil expressed volumes in terms of arbitrary standards, e.g. 'the bottle has a volume of about 18 spoonfuls'. The pupils can recall such experiences by carrying out a task such as this. Three pupils work together. Each is given a bottle of a different volume to use as an arbitrary standard in order to find the volume of a bucket. Their results can be recorded together, e.g.

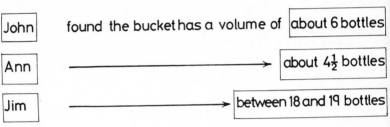

Discussion of such a result demonstrates to pupils the need for a standard that everyone is agreed upon so that measurements can be communicated and compared. The bottle which Ann has used could be such a standard—a litre. The pupils can then make a collection of containers which are marked as having a volume of about one litre, e.g. a paint tin, a jug, a detergent container, a lemonade bottle. Containers in the classroom can then be considered as having a volume of less than one litre, about one litre, or more than one litre. The teacher should try to include containers of a wide variety of shapes in such an investigation. (The litre box, a plastic cube 10cm by 10cm by 10cm, is a container which the pupils will find difficult to believe holds one litre because of its compact appearance.)

Measuring volumes in litres

Like the metre, the square metre and the kilogram, the litre is too large a unit for a great deal of practical work within the classroom. However the school and the home can provide large containers whose volumes can be measured to the nearest litre, e.g. a washhand basin, a dustbin, a metal drum could be found in school; a sink, a bath, a linen bin, at home.

Containers with a smaller volume (1 to 5 litres) are better measured to a greater degree of accuracy so if the pupil is set the task of finding the volume of a large vase or jug he may well record the result as 'about $2\frac{1}{2}$ litres' or 'nearly $3\frac{1}{4}$ litres'. Aiming for this type of result the pupil should make his own half and quarter litre measures or mark divisions on his litre container.

The ideas of ordering which have already been met in other aspects of measurement can be continued in volume. Pupils can guess the order of containers from smallest to greatest volume and then find their volumes to the nearest quarter litre. Results can then be recorded as bar charts to allow for further integration of pictorial representation and measure, e.g.

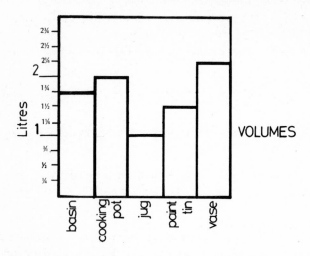

20   A universal standard of area—the square centimetre

During activities involving finding areas, it was suggested in Stage 3 that the pupil would find a preference amongst the arbitrary standards used. The square unit is liable to be the most popular because it fits together leaving no spaces and can easily be halved and quartered.

A small group of pupils should be asked to find the area of the surface of a table place-mat. Each pupil should be given a sheet of squared paper, each of which is made up of squares of a different size e.g. 5 cm, 2 cm, and 1 cm. The first pupil's sheet is marked with 2 cm squares. He draws around the mat and then counts the squares. The result is perhaps 100 square units. The pupils can now estimate the results which will be obtained using the larger squares and then the smaller squares. Each pupil should first decide if the answer will be larger or smaller than 100. Results may take the form shown opposite.

For easy counting of the smallest square, the square grid could have a red overlay of 10 cm by 10 cm and the pupil should know that each of these red squares contains 100 small ones.

From this activity the pupils will realize that it is only when the size of the square is shown or known that the result is meaningful.

AREA OF
PLACE MAT

Measure:
   100 of these squares

Guess:
   20 of these squares

Measure:
   16 of these squares

Guess:
   430 of these squares

Measure:
   400 of these squares

A universal standard which the pupils can use is the square with an edge of 1 centimetre. This is an area of one square centimetre (1cm²).

Areas in square centimetres
The pupil can carry out exercises which give him practice in drawing shapes of a specific area on centimetre-squared paper. A classmate can check these drawings, counting the squares to find the area.

Here is a worksheet example where whole and half square centimetre units are used.

Tick the shapes you think have an area of 8 cm².
Draw squares, as shown in the first shape, and
write the area of each shape.

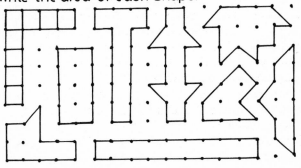

The pupil can also find the area of leaves, plastic-animal outlines and paint blots by using a square-centimetre grid on an acetate sheet. The irregularity of these outlines will demand that the pupil makes and uses a 'rule' to decide which squares he will count (see section 41, Stage 3).

An outline, e.g. of a foot or of a hand (best with closed fingers), can be drawn on centimetre-squared paper and these areas counted. With these larger areas the approximate nature of measure is re-emphasized as two pupils counting the same area are liable to obtain different answers. Discussion can take place as to how different answers can arise and still come within an acceptable range.

21   A universal standard of weight—the kilogram

By now pupils are probably ready to accept the need for a standard unit of weight so the kilogram should be introduced. This is quite a large unit for classroom use and the teacher should prepare some packages so that the pupils can select ones of about one kilogram, just over a kilogram and just under a kilogram.

Weighing in kilograms

A set of personal scales will allow the pupils to read their weight to the nearest kilogram. Reading a scale is likely to be a new skill and so the pupil must be given the opportunity of understanding the markings and the weight that each interval represents before being asked to use the scales.

Results for a group or class of pupils can be expressed in a bar chart. When weighing heavier packages on the classroom balance, the pupil should have the opportunity of using $\frac{1}{2}$ kilogram and $\frac{1}{4}$ kilogram weights and in consequence expressing results to the nearest $\frac{1}{4}$ kg.

A collection of groceries in 1kg, $\frac{1}{2}$kg and $\frac{1}{4}$kg packs should be made so that the pupil is not only relating these standards to the metal weights used with the classroom balance, but is also comparing them with standard packages. Estimation of weight is difficult and so the pupils should realize that their estimates are liable to be more wide ranging than in other measures.

The gram

Another standard of weight is the gram. This is a fine unit and the pupil should not be asked to weigh to the nearest gram.

By balancing a kilogram with marked commercial weights the pupil will find 1000gm = 1kg.

Weighing can also be associated with project work on postal costs and with cooking and baking. The teacher can select and adapt recipes which are suitable for classroom use. The pupils would enjoy compiling their own recipe book.

22   Time to the nearest five minutes

Reading around the clock intervals recalls the multiples of five. The movement of the large hand can be expressed in minutes giving the pupil practice in reading, recording and showing times such as 'five-twenty', '5.20', 'twenty past five'. The pupil has to be introduced to expressions such as 'twenty minutes to six' as an equivalent of '5.40'. Worksheet examples of clock faces can be labelled with two expressions, e.g. 4.55, five to five.

When the pupil is drawing clock hands the larger one should be easily distinguished from the smaller and the position of the small hour hand should be appropriate to the minute hand, i.e. at five to the hour, the hour hand is almost at the hour mark whereas at twenty-five past it is almost half way between two hour numbers.

The times for television programmes are usually expressed as 7.15, 8.20 etc. The format for the hour varies with 10.0 and 10.00 both being found and the pupils can discuss this and then write out their ideal evening's viewing from 4.30 till 10.05.

23   am and pm

When a pupil is looking at television times he may be confused by the use of a time such as 7.15 twice in the same day. It can be explained that the letters am and pm often follow the time to show clearly whether it is morning or afternoon. The pupil will recall that the hour hand travels around the clock face twice every day, i.e. that there are twenty-four hours in one day. The first revolution occurs before midday or antemeridian and the second begins at midday. Afternoon and evening times are regarded as postmeridian i.e. after midday.

Pupils can be given the task of writing an invitation or a letter which states times of events where it is important that the reader should know if it is am or pm that is being mentioned.

24   Twenty-four hour notation

When the pupil is looking for the expressions am and pm in timetables, he will find times stated as 14.15, 21.40 etc. It can then be explained that it is also possible to count the second revolution of the hour hand as a continuation after 12 to 13, 14 etc. Many digital clocks and watches use this notation. If possible, the teacher should use a digital clock to show what happens when the clock is wound past 11 pm towards midnight. 23.59 moves to 00.00 not to 24.00 so that the clock is ready to record the new day.

The pupil should be given practice in using local train and bus timetables, e.g. 'Which train would you catch to meet a friend in Glasgow at 10 am? Which train would you catch to be home in time for tea at 5.30 pm?' This type of assignment is realistic and leads to discussion about times taken to reach the station, buy tickets etc.

SHAPE
The pupil should be able to:
25   sort three-dimensional shapes according to the shape of face, number of faces, edges, corners
26   investigate the edges, and corners (angles) of polygons with less than or six edges.

25   More three-dimensional shapes
Cartons or models of these shapes should be collected:

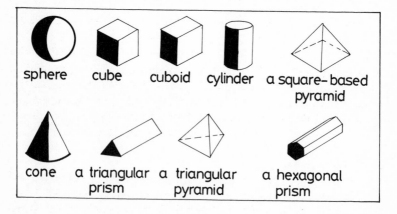

The pupil will be familiar with seven of these shapes from the previous stages. The triangular pyramid and the hexagonal prism are likely to be new shapes or at least new names. Such names can lead to a discussion of why these names are appropriate. Describing three-dimensional shapes should now include the shapes of the faces, e.g. a cylinder has two flat circle faces, one curved face which can open out into a rectangle, two curved edges and no corners.

'In the bag' game
This game encourages such oral descriptions. A pupil selects one of the
shapes of the collected set from a box and places it in a bag, unseen by
the other pupils. The pupil sits facing the others, the bag with its hidden
shape in his hand. The pupils ask questions in order to identify the shape.
These questions can only be answered by 'Yes' or 'No'.

This game may well be based more on guessing names than on reasoning through data or properties, but if the teacher joins in, she will be able
to direct the questioning along a sequenced pattern about faces, edges
and corners.

26   Edges and corners of polygons
From a set of flat shapes the pupil can try to order shapes by the number
of their edges, e.g.

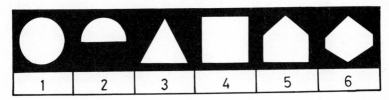

An investigation of how many diagonals can be drawn can be carried
out and recorded. (A diagonal joins nonadjacent corners.)

The pupil has already met the square corner—this can also be called a
right angle. The pupil can use a square corner to test the corners of other
shapes and to find those which also have right angles. The pupil can also
test corners of objects in the classroom to find right angles, e.g. the
window, the blackboard, the door, the book, the table.

This shape game will consolidate the work of this section.

'Match this shape' game
Two-dimensional shapes are drawn on a set of cards. The pack of forty
cards could contain two of each of the shapes shown on page 202.
The pack of cards is shuffled and then dealt to the players. Each player
matches the shapes of his cards to find as many pairs as possible. The
pairs are placed face down in front of the player. Each player is left with
a set of unmatched cards. The task is now to obtain a match from the
other players by a series of interchanges, e.g.

Joe: 'Jim, do you have a shape with three edges?'
Jim: 'Yes'
Joe: 'Are all the edges straight?'

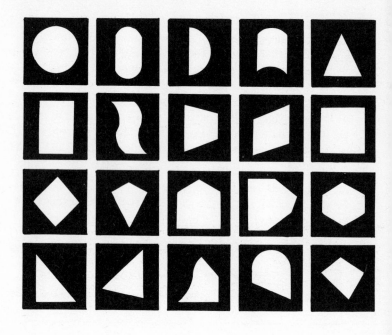

Jim: 'Yes'
Joe: 'Is one corner of the triangle a right angle?'
Jim: 'Yes'
Joe: 'Can I have the right-angled triangle please?'

The first player has obtained a match for one of his cards and can now place this pair on the table in front of him. If he had been unsuccessful because Jim did not have the required card, the player who *does* have the card now knows who to ask when his turn comes. The player who is first to find a match for all his cards, and with his pairs checked as correct, is the winner.

PICTORIAL REPRESENTATION
The pupil should be able to:
27   construct and interpret simple bar charts with a vertical scale.

27   Bar charts
In Stage 3, the pupil was concerned with block graphs where one item of

data was represented by one square on a graph. In this section of work, the concept of a vertical scale is introduced.

The pupils are given a box of coloured pencils and asked to construct a graph of colours where each pencil is represented by a Cuisenaire unit cube. The completed graph with cubes laid out on a sheet of paper looks like this:

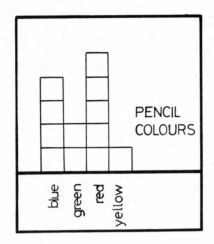

The teacher can suggest to the pupils that the unit cubes be replaced by Cuisenaire rods of the appropriate length. These rods are then outlined on the paper so that the graph now looks like this:

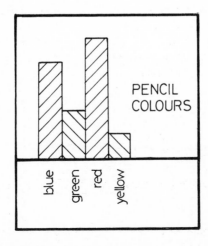

It is now possible to tell that there are more red pencils than yellow ones but difficult to state how many more. A scale at the left-hand side solves this problem (1 cm represents one pencil on this scale).

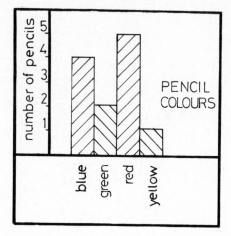

The pupils can now construct and interpret several bar charts of this type. Here is a graph showing the number of edges of the shapes on the forty cards for the 'Match this shape' game (section 26):

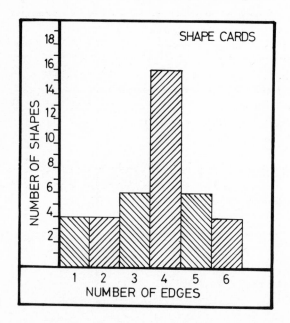

From this graph the pupil can calculate how many more shapes have four edges than have three edges, how many shapes are represented on the graph etc.

Data about larger numbers can lead the teacher and pupils to discuss the possibility of marking a scale in twos, threes, fives or even tens. Cars in a local car park might be represented as shown in this graph:

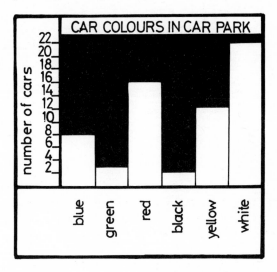

With a scale such as the one illustrated, the pupil should be shown how to read off the 'value' of the 'bar' using a ruler. This is especially important when the number represented involves a fraction of the scale interval, e.g. there are three green cars shown in the graph. If accurate readings for values are required, the pupils should mark, though not number, all whole numbers on the scale.

Reference
Some of the recording formats, e.g. in division, can be linked to those used in the series *Primary Mathematics* (Scottish Primary Mathematics Group, Heinemann Educational, 1975).